THE
TACHOGRAPH
MANUAL

THE TACHOGRAPH MANUAL

SECOND EDITION

DAVID LOWE

KOGAN
PAGE

First edition published as 'The Tachograph' in 1982 by Fleet Planning Limited, Church House, Hampton in Arden, Solihull B92 0EX.

Second edition first published in 1989 by Kogan Page Ltd, 120 Pentonville Rd, London N1 9JN

Printed and bound in Great Britain by Richard Clay Ltd, Bungay, Suffolk.

British Library Cataloguing in Publication Data
Lowe, David, 1936—
   The tachograph manual. – 2nd ed.
   1. Commercial vehicles. Tachographs
   I. Title
   622.2'73

ISBN 1-85091-933-X

Contents

The Author 7

Foreword 9

Preface 11

Acknowledgements 13

Introduction 15

1 The Tachograph Instrument 19
2 Installation and Calibration of Tachographs 33
3 Charts and Recordings 43
4 Chart Filing and Storage Systems 51
5 Chart Analysis Equipment – Manual and Electronic 53
6 Computerised Chart Analysis 60
7 Checking Charts for Legal Purposes 65
8 Chart Analysis for Operational Purposes 70
9 Accident Evaluation from Charts 87
10 The Driver, Tachographs and Productivity 99
11 Tachographs in Transport Planning 106
12 Chart Recordings in Practice 116
13 How Tachograph Law Applies in the UK 132
14 Offences, Penalties, Defences, Enforcement Powers and Legal Proceedings in the UK 142
15 Tachograph-Related Vehicle Equipment – New Technology Developments 148

Appendices
I Tachograph Legislation (EC 3821/85) 162
II Exemptions from Tachograph Fitment and Use (UK Derogations) 179
III Summary of EC Drivers' Hours Law (EC 3820/85) 182
IV Bibliography of Relevant UK Legislation 186
V Tachographs and UK Annual Vehicle Testing 187
VI Approved Tachograph Centres in the UK 189
VII Useful Addresses 215

Index *219*
Index of Advertisers *224*

The Author

David Lowe is well known in the transport industry as a consultant lecturer and writer. He has carried out consultancy projects for many nationally-known companies. His lecturing programme covers a variety of transport topics and he has addressed national and international conferences in this country and abroad as well as running many in-company training sessions on transport-related subjects.

He is the author of *The Transport Manager's and Operator's Handbook*, currently in its 19th annual edition and looked upon as the 'bible' of legal requirements by many operators, and many other books including *A Study Manual of Professional Competence in Road Transport Management, The Goods Vehicle Costing and Pricing Handbook* and the predecessor to this book *The Tachograph*.

For many years Mr Lowe has maintained a particular interest in the subject of tachographs. He has studied their use in detail and kept abreast of developments over the past 20 years. The subject has been included in his lecturing programme for a number of years and at the time of their mandatory introduction in Britain in 1979/1981 he presented a very large number of public and in-company seminars and training sessions for company managements, supervisory and driving staffs, giving him a valuable insight to the problems of understanding and interpretation of both the complexities of the legislation and the technicalities of the application and use of the instrument.

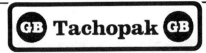

Foreword

The Tachograph Manual was first published in 1981, a year when the installation of tachographs to upwards of half a million commercial vehicles including coaches, trucks and vans was completed. Prior to legislation, the emphasis had been on educating both vehicle operators and drivers not only about the use of the instrument as a log to record the activities of the driver, but as a tool to improve the efficiency of the transport operator.

In the early 1980s most of the tachographs in use were mechanically driven from the vehicle gearbox and care had to be taken to use only the best equipment installed by properly trained personnel. Today all new vehicles are equipped with electronically-driven tachographs with self-diagnostic features which form part of a modern, ergonomic and aesthetically pleasing vehicle instrument panel. Nevertheless, it is still important that the rules surrounding the installation and use of the system be properly understood and it is a feature of the UK legislation that about 500 Department of Transport tachograph centres are authorised to provide information and support.

While the bulk of *The Tachograph Manual* has required only minor modification to reflect changes in the regulations or in product design, the emphasis on correct use of the data carried on the chart is changing. More operators are interested in checking vehicle road speed in the interests of safety and economy and in the hope that road speed limiter legislation, already in force on coaches, will not be required for heavy commercial vehicles. More combined road and engine speed tachographs are being sold, again in the interests of protecting vehicle operators' investment by encouraging careful and sensible driving. The latest tachographs have the facility to download such data directly to the office computer. By 1992, the trade barriers will be down in Europe, requiring even greater efforts from vehicle operators to compete and the tachograph will assist in this.

The focus must now be on deriving maximum benefit from the tachograph to ensure that fleet management systems relevant to each business are installed and used. The continuing co-operation of drivers must be extended so that as tachographs are increasingly complemented by in-cab computers, hand-held terminals, mobile telephones etc, particularly in large vehicle fleets, the transition to more sophisticated systems is made effectively and as painlessly as possible.

To get this important transition right, the preparation must be right. For this reason I have no hesitation in recommending *The Tachograph Manual* to those in the industry who want to check that they are on the right track, and to students and others everywhere who are in or are thinking of making a career in transportation.

Fred Kay
Managing Director
Lucas Kienzle Instruments Limited

Preface

In 1979 when preparatory work was in progress on introducing the necessary legislation in Britain to enforce EC requirements for the compulsory fitment and use of tachographs in most goods vehicles over 3.5 tonnes gross weight, I published the original version of *The Tachograph Manual*. The purpose of the Manual was to set out in some detail the basic information relating to tachographs which fleet operators, transport managers, vehicle drivers, and indeed anybody else concerned with transport would need to know in order to understand and comply with the then proposed legislation.

This was followed in 1981 by a much more substantial work called *The Tachograph* (published by my company Fleet Planning Limited) containing much of the material published in the earlier work but updated to include the latest legislation and the then current uderstanding of the subject. It was, however, further expanded to include much more information on the economics of tachographs, their use in fleet control, their role in productivity and bonus schemes, the nature of chart analysis both manually and with more sophisticated systems and accident evaluation.

Overall, the purpose was to provide a comprehensive work on the subject of tachographs. Regrettably, however, as those people who have been long in the industry will know, neither time, the legislators, nor those who make the definitive interpretations of legal requirements will pause long enough for operators to catch their breath before new requirements, new understandings and new developments need their attention.

So it is that while the aim for the book was clear then, the progress of time and all that goes with it has invalidated that aim, hence the time has come for the publication of yet another new and updated edition. This new edition, returning to the original title, has been revised to include current EC legislation and present-day knowledge of the subject in practice and to reflect continuing operator requirements for a detailed explanation of the whole subject in one comprehensive document. The sequence of contents has been changed to provide material relating to the practical aspects of the instrument and its use ahead of the explanation of the legal requirements.

It is important to mention here that while tachograph instruments themselves and the practical aspects of their fitment and use have changed only marginally apart from the legislative changes, the newly emerging vehicle-based information technology industry is expanding rapidly and dramatically, reflecting significant developments in microchip technology. So now, although the tachograph as we currently know it will not go away because the law will not permit it to do so, the current development emphasis is on in-cab or on-board computers and other vehicle-mounted monitoring equipment (fuel consumption metering, for example). For this reason I have taken the opportunity with a new edition to include a section on this subject. It is only possible to give the reader a brief outline appreciation here and indicate the direction in which developments may be expected. But this is an exciting and rapidly developing area which the progressively minded transport operator will want to follow closely unless he is to be left far behind in the quest for a secure place in this ever-more technology oriented and highly competitive industry.

However, it is also important to recognise that the real purpose of the book is to provide a practical explanation of the tachograph, its installation and use, as it exists in thousands of vehicles today. New technology is fine for those who want it and can afford it. Many operators feel it is of little interest to them and certainly outside their present-day operating budgets. Students and others with transport industry interests will also find the book to be of use to them.

A further significant change has been made since the previous edition. This is a fundamental re-direction of emphasis in the nature and structure of the text to reflect potential interest in the book among the operators in the wider European market for whom exactly the same EC tachograph regulations apply and for whom therefore the explanations of the legislation and of fitment and use of the instruments and analysis of charts will be of equal interest.

Finally, a most significant change, from the author's point of view, is that publication of the book has now been kindly taken over by Kogan Page Limited who will use their considerable experience of the transport books market and expertise in direct mail selling of technical books to promote this edition to a much wider readership.

Overall, I hope this new edition will prove to be both interesting and useful as a work of reference for all those in both British and European transport operations who in any way are or may become involved with tachograph use.

David Lowe
February 1989

Acknowledgements

My knowledge of the subject of tachographs has developed over many years during which time association with large numbers of people involved both with the manufacture and the use of the instrument has contributed greatly to what I have been able to include in this work. As much as I would like to individually acknowledge all this help I regret I cannot for reasons of space and for fear that I may inadvertently omit to name somebody who made a worthy contribution. But some people must be named because without them this book or its predecessors would have never appeared.

I must refer particularly to my long-standing association with Lucas Kienzle Instruments Limited in Britain and Kienzle Apparate GmbH (now Mannesmann Kienzle GmbH) in West Germany and to my friendship with many of the senior executives of both companies, especially Fred Kay of Lucas Kienzle (who most kindly contributed a Foreword to this new edition) and Gerhard Toeter, Klaus Thede and Walter Eith of Kienzle. Their co-operation and guidance over many years has been invaluable and to them personally I offer a special word of thanks.

Finally, but certainly not least, I must acknowledge the support of my wife Patricia who has endured the rigours of my absence on lecture tours and early morning, late night and weekend writing sessions.

Acknowledgement for Illustrations

Many of the illustrations in this Manual are taken from the literature of Mannesmann Kienzle GmbH, West Germany and Lucas Kienzle Instruments Limited of Birmingham and to both companies I wish to express my gratitude for their kind permission to reproduce this material.

Author's Note

This book contains many mentions, descriptions and illustrations of products and services related to the West German tachograph manufacturer Kienzle. The reason is that this name represents the original manufacturer of these instruments, the leader in developing tachograph and related equipment technology, the most widely-known tachograph make worldwide (and incidentally the world's largest producer of parking and taxi meters), and the supplier of some 85 per cent of the original tachograph equipment fitment to vehicles sold in Britain. As a company it produces excellent and comprehensive support data and literature which it has kindly permitted me to use as acknowledged above. Thus it is just not possible to write on this subject without featuring the name prominently. However, it should be made clear to the reader that despite the help given and the use of material as indicated this book is *not* sponsored by or intended as publicity for either Mannesmann Kienzle GmbH in West Germany or Lucas Kienzle Instruments Limited in the UK. It is written quite independently and the views and interpretations expressed are those of the author alone except where otherwise stated.

David Lowe
February 1989

Introduction

Although written in Britain with UK experience and practices very much in mind, this book covers the subject of tachographs on a European-wide basis. The principal legislative requirements for their use apply equally to goods and passenger vehicle operators and drivers in all 12 EC member states as do the practical aspects of fitment and use of the instruments and of chart interpretation and analysis. The largest manufacturer of tachograph instruments and analysis equipment is West German and much of the operating experience with tachographs and with scientific analysis of the recordings made was developed in that country.

In Britain, interest in and concern about tachographs really began with the 1968 Transport Act. The Act proposed that the then new system of driver's hours requirements should be regulated by the use of a recording instrument (viz. a tachograph) installed in heavy goods and passenger vehicles. Prior to this there were many transport operators who were familiar with the old type of time recorder (notably manufactured by Servis) and a number who used the conventional tachograph instrument as we know it today, albeit the instruments we are now talking of are somewhat different from earlier models insofar as for legal purposes they all now have to comply with an EC specification.

Historically, tachographs date back to 1927 when they were first used in Germany in the form that we know them today (ie recording time, distance and speed) although, of course, there have been substantial developments and refinements incorporated since then. The instruments were used extensively in Germany until they became a compulsory fitment by law in that country in goods vehicles over 7.5 tonnes gross weight in 1953. In Britain, the subject raised great controversy following publication of the 1968 Transport Act. Although the particular provisions contained in that Act were not implemented at the time a strong body of adversaries – principally the trade unions, a proportion of heavy goods vehicle drivers plus, to a certain extent, the two main transport associations and some of the transport operators which they represent – warned consistently of the dangers, difficulties and high costs which would result from a statutory fitment and use policy.

Such opinions were not, however, universal throughout the transport industry in Britain and there were firms who had operated the instruments satisfactorily and with worthwhile benefits to themselves and their drivers for a number of years. In most cases such firms were operating with specific agreement from union representatives or at least with their general approval, but in order to avoid the difficulties which may have confronted them in certain quarters they 'kept their heads down' and attempted to attract as little publicity as possible to ensure uninterrupted operation prior to legislative compulsion.

As a member of the European Economic Community Britain was obliged under the Treaty of Rome to fall in line with the general requirements to fit and use tachographs. Initially dates were set for fitment and use to commence in 1976 but these plans were postponed while Britain resolved other problems, not least the basic decision of whether or not we remained in the EC which was finally decided in the affirmative by a national referendum. The need for economic restraint at the time was also put forward as a reason for not following the originally proposed timetable. Britain's failure to meet the EC requirement on this issue resulted in infraction proceedings and a judgment early in 1979 by the European Court of Justice that we must comply. With some obvious reluctance the British Government accepted the inevitability of this and on 5 March 1979, Transport Minister Mr William Rodgers announced in Parliament that we would comply.

In the author's view, there have always been two alternative approaches which could be adopted by operators faced with the obligation to fit tachographs. They can incur the cost of supply, fitment and calibration of the instrument and its drive mechanism and they can buy charts, supply them to drivers and collect them after use, and then give them a cursory glance to satisfy the minimum requirements of the law for employers to check driver's records. On this basis the cost of tachographs will be seen to be another burden of expense caused through compulsory legislative measures and, as such, acceptable only under protest.

On the other hand, operators can accept the costs of tachographs and take a more positive view of the whole issue, seeking to utilise the benefits which must accrue from having available much more precise operating data than hitherto. There is no doubt that the information obtained from chart analysis enables the operator to plan and control vehicle activities more efficiently and that this increased efficiency provides positive and recognisable financial benefits which considerably exceed the on-going costs of tachograph operation. Furthermore, many operators who had already used tachographs for a period prior to legislative compulsion quickly realised benefits, such as reductions in fuel consumption, which resulted from the driver's interest in the charts and the facility to assess good and bad driving techniques.

Whichever of these two alternative attitudes are adopted this book should help the operator to understand the law, how the instrument works and what the recordings show and, in addition, what economic and operational benefits may be gained from exploiting its use as a management tool. The introduction of the tachograph could be said to have heralded a new era in transport management but this will only be so if a positive and concerted effort is made by all parties to work towards this end. But this is only the beginning. Developing microchip technology is opening up new opportunities for increased use of 'information technology' deriving from other vehicle-mounted equipment and in-cab (on-board if you prefer the American variation of the term) computers. So while the tachograph instrument as we currently know it, and its recording chart – both respectively being extremely antiquated by today's 'hi-tec' standards – must remain with us for many years to come because of the legal connotations (and the law changes very, very slowly as the reader will know and appreciate) there are parallel and overlapping developments using the very latest techniques and technologies which present the vehicle fleet operator with exciting possibilities for fleet monitoring and control which were unthinkable only a year or two ago.

Thus the reader will find this book useful in providing him with all the essential groundwork on tachograph use but also interesting for the way in which it points him towards these developing technologies, many of them so dynamic that no sooner are they announced that they become 'old hat' and replaced by yet another new generation of ideas and hardware.

1: The Tachograph Instrument

Tachographs as we currently recognise them were first produced in Germany in 1928 and in the period 1936/37 Daimler-Benz and Krupp became the first vehicle manufacturers to fit the instrument as standard equipment. By 1938 the first fully-flush dash-board fitting instruments were in use. Development of the tachograph has progressed since that time to the instrument we know today. In 1972 the first electronic tachograph was produced and 1973 saw the commencement of production of instruments conforming to the EC specification set out originally in Annex 1 to EC Regulation 1463/70 which has since been replaced by EC Regulation 3821/85 (see Appendix I).

Technology, and especially development of the microchip, has reached a point today which makes the conventional tachograph, its method of recording and the chart itself completely outmoded. However, despite the increasing interest in and considerable development of 'hi-tec' on-board information origination facilities, and of data storage and transmission systems, European legislation currently demands that we stay with the present tachograph system as the basic means of recording drivers' activities in relation to driving and other work activities, breaks and rest periods. While operators may fit and use the more modern and more sophisticated equipment as they wish when it become available, they must not do so in a way which usurps the legal precedence of the conventional tachograph recording system. Thus they must continue to fit and use tachographs as required by law. This may be no bad thing for the owner-driver and small fleets, but the trade association view is that a choice should be permitted between the use of a tachograph or an in-cab computer for law-enforcement purposes.

The Instrument

The tachograph is an instrument – usually mounted in the vehicle cab – designed to indicate to the driver the three functions of time, speed and distance and to record movement of the vehicle, the speeds at which it travelled and the distance covered. Information is recorded on a special chart against a 24-hour time scale.

A variety of instrument makes are to be found in British and European fleets. Principally these are Kienzle (manufactured in West Germany and marketed in the UK by Lucas Kienzle Instruments), Smiths (Jaeger instruments made in France – but branded as Smiths – and at one time marketed in the UK by Smiths Industries), Veeder-Root (American-owned company manufacturing in Scotland), Jaeger (French manufactured and marketed in the UK by Time Instrument Manufacturers Limited) and Moto-meter (West German manufacture – no manufacture or recognised supply source in the UK but some reconditioning of instruments being carried out).

One- and Two-Man Tachographs

While a variety of different types of EC approved tachographs are available, the principal differences are between one- and two-man instruments, between standard operation and automatic instruments and between cable driven and electronic drive instruments.

For vehicles which are *never* to be driven by more than one crew man, a one-man tachograph will suffice. Such an instrument carries only one chart and has a single switch on the outer casing for the driver to select and indicate his various activity modes. Few one-man tachographs are now sold because of the universal demand for two man versions.

When vehicles are to be driven by more than one crew member (ie driver and mate) even if this is only a rare possibility then a two-man tachograph must be fitted to provide the mandatory records needed by both crew members.

The two-man instrument has a means of accommodating two charts: one in a primary position to accept recordings of driving time, speed and distance plus other work, break and rest periods in respect of the driver or number one crew member's activities and one in a secondary position to accept recording of time only in respect of the passenger or number two crew member's activities (ie other work, break or rest periods). Two activity mode switches are mounted on the face of the instrument, one for the driver and the other for the second crew member, enabling both to indicate their activities by selecting the appropriate switch positions. While driver one is behind the wheel, with his chart in the primary position and his switch turned to the driving mode position a full range of recordings will be made on his chart. At the same time, driver two, currently riding passenger, with his chart in the secondary position has his switch turned to the 'attendance at work' position and this produces a time trace only on the appropriate section of the chart. When crew members change position they must also change the position of their charts and change over use of the switches to ensure correct and accurate recordings for both of them.

If a two-man instrument is used by a single driver, with Kienzle instruments a special blind chart (ie a plain plastic disc) should be inserted in the instrument in the secondary position to protect the styli from long-term damage and to prevent the red fascia warning light glowing (which indicates to the driver that his instrument is not fully operational). With Veeder-Root instruments the driver also has a warning light to indicate if the chart is missing (on the latest instruments). The driver is able to determine by looking at the face of the instrument without opening it that either a chart is not in place or that the instrument is not recording properly by means of:

1. a red warning light (Kienzle instruments)
2. a window on top of the instrument (Jaeger-type and Veeder-Root instruments)

Figure 1.1   *Latest generation Lucas Kienzle two-man automatic tachograph instrument*

Figure 1.2   *Modern heavy vehicle dashboard (Volvo) with automatic tachograph head installed*

On top of the instrument is the key hole which accepts a fully universal key, fitting all makes and type of tachograph, for opening the face.

Drive Systems

Mechanical Drive System

Generally, the instrument is driven by a flexible drive shaft from the vehicle transmission gearbox connected through an adaptor gearbox and, in some cases, a two-speed adaptor for taking account of changing rear-axle ratios. The adaptor gearbox and the two-speed adaptor are intended to correct the drive ratio to ensure that speed and distance recordings are within the permitted installation and use tolerances of:

1. Speed   ±4 and ±6 kilometres per hour more or less than the real speed respectively,
2. Distance   ±2 and ±4 per cent more or less than the real distance of at least one kilometre respectively.

Electronic Drive System

Alternatively, tachographs may be electronically driven and all new vehicles in recent times have been fitted with this version. The principal advantages of this type of instrument are the elimination of defect-prone corrector gearboxes and cable drive systems and the possibility of having excess electronic cable coiled on the chassis so seals do not have to be broken when, for example, removing a gearbox to carry out clutch repairs. With a conventional drive cable seal breakage and cable disconnection is inevitable for clutch repairs thus necessitating extra time and cost (downtime, travel to the tachograph centre and sealing costs) to get the installation put back into a 'legal' condition. Initially the electronic instrument was designed with fitment to rear-engined coaches in mind to avoid long cable runs. However, goods vehicle operators saw the advantages of the system and many of them considered the additional cost to be well justified when compared to the downtime and re-sealing costs incurred with conventional cable drive systems.

Electronic tachographs fall into two categories: earlier system versions which use electronic pulse generators or impulse transmitters, regulators and drive motors and the latest systems which use a microprocessor. The use of a microprocessor gives reliable service and accurate display and recording of time, speed and distance travelled.

System calibration with these later systems is achieved within the tachograph head by adjusting the digital input to the microprocessor. Therefore the ratio corrector box is eliminated and the number of seals considerably reduced. Use of the self-checking speed transducer input to the microprocessor, via a simple wire, replaces the flexible mechanical-drive cable. With this system the route from the transducer to the head is no longer important. With the pulse generator type of instrument a series of signals is sent to the electronic regulator based on the output

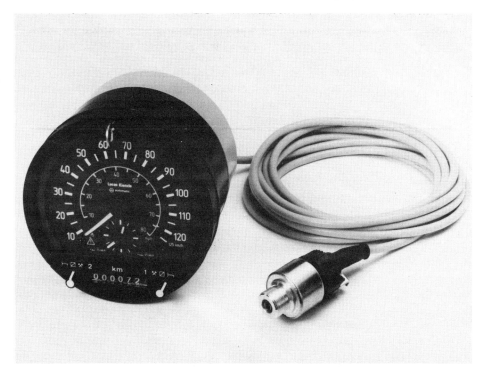

Figure 1.3 *Automatic tachograph showing electronic cable drive and sensor unit*

revolutions from the vehicle gearbox. These signals or pulses are processed by the regulator to drive the tachograph motor. The tachograph motor in its turn sends back signals to the regulator and compensation required is self-monitored and synchronous.

Recording Mechanism

Records are made on tachograph charts by means of three styli (some of which are sapphire tipped), one for each function:

1. Speed
2. Time
3. Distance

A fourth stylus is sometimes included as an operator option if additional (non-statutory) recordings are required (see p 50).

When a chart is inserted in the instrument it is carried round by the clock mechanism and, so long as the clock continues to operate and the face of the instrument is closed, records are continuously made by means of the styli engraving a trace on the chart surface. It should be noted that if the chart is left in the instrument for more than 24 hours records will overrun areas of the chart on which previous recordings were made causing confusion and difficulty in analysis and contravening the regulations. Conversely, if the face of the instrument is left open there will be gaps in the recording equal to the time of opening. This too will create suspicion among enforcement staffs since it is illegal to have any unexplained breaks in the recording.

Recording While Stationary

While the vehicle is stationary, the time stylus makes a recording on the appropriate section of the chart depending on the activity mode indicated by the number 1 switch on the face of the instrument as follows:

Standard Tachographs

1. Driving (if the switch is left in this position while the vehicle is stationary a thin trace will be produced in the driving radial but it will be clear that the vehicle was not moving at the time).
2. Attendance at work (covering non-driving activities).
3. Break and rest periods.

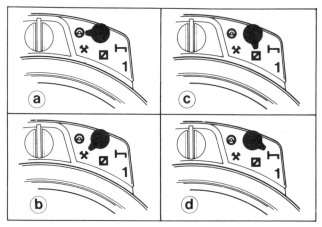

Figure 1.4   *Standard tachograph modes (a) Driving mode (b) Active work mode (not used in the UK) (c) Passive work mode (used in the UK for attendance at work ie for all work other than driving) (d) Break and rest period mode*

Most instruments have a facility for recording against the cross-hammers symbol which is used in Europe to indicate 'active' work as opposed to 'passive' work (ie the symbol referred to in 2 above) but this activity group is not legally required to be used in the UK.

Automatic Tachographs

1. Driving is only recorded when the vehicle moves and the driver does not need to select this mode – it is done automatically for him. When the vehicle is stationary a recording appropriate to the activity at which the switch is pointing will be made (ie crossed hammers, attendance at work or break).

2. Attendance at work.
3. Break and rest periods. *See note above about crossed hammers recording.*

At the same time, with both standard and automatic-type tachographs the speed stylus produces a continuous trace following the base line of the speed recording on the chart. Similarly, the distance stylus continues to indicate a trace on the appropriate area of the chart on a constant radius from the point reached when the vehicle last moved.

Recordings While Moving
As soon as the vehicle moves, three separate recording activities commence:

1. The speed stylus begins to move upwards recording the vehicle's acceleration and subsequent fluctuations in speed during its travel until it slows to a standstill when the stylus returns again to the base line position.
2. The distance stylus begins to move over a limited path upwards and down-

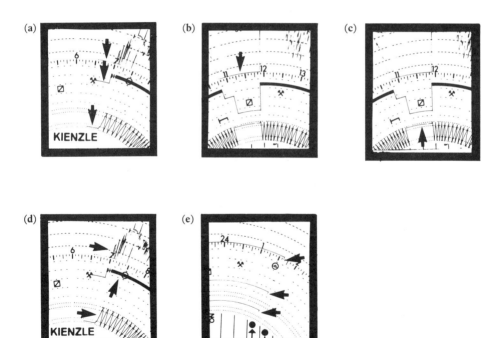

Figure 1.5   (*a*) *While vehicle is stationary the styli record as indicated* (*b*) *Note speed stylus records on base line when vehicle is stopped* (*c*) *Distance stylus maintains its position while vehicle is stationary* (*d*) *All three styli start recording when vehicle moves* (*e*) *Tell-tale marks are made when the face of the instrument is opened*

wards, commencing where it was positioned when the vehicle last moved and continuing in the same direction. At the top and bottom of each stroke it changes direction, making a recording equivalent to five kilometres for each individual upward stroke and another five kilometres for each downward stroke. When the vehicle stops, the stylus also stops moving and retains its position until the vehicle next moves.

3. The time group recording stylus begins to oscillate rapidly up and down at speed, creating a broad running trace on the chart (except on Veeder-Root instruments). As soon as the vehicle stops, the stylus returns to its static position, making a single fine trace in the appropriate section of the chart.

    Note: The running trace is created irrespective of the position in which the activity mode switch is left so that failure to turn the switch to the correct (driving) mode does not prevent recording of vehicle running although such recording may be made on the wrong part of the time group recording area. This is an offence.

The tachograph is provided with a facility to indicate, by marks on the chart, every time the instrument face is opened. This helps to distinguish the time and frequency of authorised and unauthorised opening of the instrument.

Recordings for Second Crew Member

In the case of two-man instruments, simultaneous recordings are made on the second crew member's chart by means of a mechanically operated stylus (or motor operated on automatic-type instruments) linked to the number 2 activity mode switch. This is positioned to indicate the activity on which the second crew member is engaged – attendance at work or break or rest period. No recordings of speed or distance travelled, or indication of the vehicle movement is made on the second position chart. When crew members change over the driving position, it is essential that they change the position of their respective record charts; the number one driver putting his in the secondary position and the number two driver placing his in the primary position to accept recordings of time, speed and distance. They must also change over use of the switch so the person driving always used the number 1 switch.

Recording Method

The various traces described previously are made on the special pressure sensitive recording layer (generally described as wax) on the face of the paper chart. Each stylus makes a distinct and clearly engraved trace (not an ink marking) sufficiently accurately scribed and positioned on the chart to enable subsequent analysis to determine movement and speed of the vehicle and other driver activities to within seconds and metres.

Inserting Charts

To insert a chart in the tachograph, the instrument is opened by turning the key and pulling the face forward. This exposes the interior of the instrument and, on

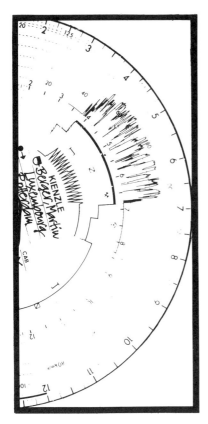 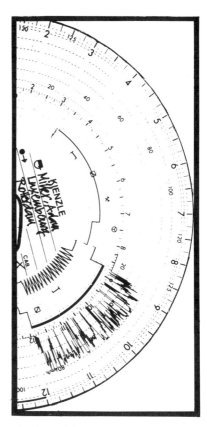

Figure 1.6 *Simultaneous recording of two crew members' activities*

the inside of the face, the clock-mounted central pillar on which the chart is mounted. The chart is held with the sensitised recording surface uppermost, and then placed over the central pillar revolving it as necessary to properly locate in a 'time right' position over the pillar and any locating pegs. A holding collar or clip must usually be placed over the chart to secure its position unless the instrument is of a type which provides for automatic chart retention when the face of the instrument is closed. In the case of two-man instruments, the second crew member inserts his chart first, securing it in position, enabling the driver to then insert his chart as described above. With the charts in position the instrument face can be closed and the key turned to secure it. Removal of the used chart is by the reverse procedure.

Setting the Clock

It is the driver's legal responsibility to ensure that the clock in his tachograph instrument is set to the right time (ie the correct time in the country of registration of the vehicle). This is done either by turning the knurled wheel on the inside of the instrument face (on Kienzle, Jaeger and latest Veeder-Root instruments) or by using the detachable, bayonet fitting, chart retaining collar (on earlier Veeder-Root instruments) which also has a built-in clock adjuster.

To insert the chart correctly, first the driver should look to see what time is shown on the outer edge of the chart nearest to the key position because this is where the recordings start. It this time is correct in accordance with the 24-hour clock then it will ensure that recordings are made on the right time section of the chart (ie day or night). Second, he must look at the face of the clock to get the time precisely right in hours and minutes.

Speed Warning Light

Most tachographs are fitted with a speed warning light in the face of the instrument or on the shoulder (Veeder-Root) which illuminates when the vehicle is driven in excess of a predetermined speed. The speed at which the light operates is selected by a screw, slide or button inside the instrument. This has an indicator alongside to show the speed selected. On all occasions when the vehicle speed exceeds the pre-set speed the speed light comes on and remains on until the vehicle speeds falls. Since this light is not part of the legal requirements there is no legal requirement for it to be set in any particular position – usually is is set to 80kph (approx 50mph) at the time of official calibration – so the driver or operator may alter it if he wishes to any other speed to suit his particular requirements. If company policy stipulates restricted speeds for its vehicles or a set speed for the light to operate then examination of speed recordings on the driver's chart will readily show that the stipulated speed limit has been exceeded.

Failure Warnings Systems

Various methods are provided by tachograph manufactures to indicate to the driver that recordings are not being made or that there is a fault in the instrument. In all cases the driver can observe that the speedometer is functioning, also that the odometer is functioning by observing the rotation of the coloured one-tenth km scale and that the clock indicator (a coloured disc which is seen through an apperture in the face of, or near to, the clock) is rotating properly. To ensure that a recording is being made the driver can observe the further failure warning systems provided. The Kienzle system uses a red warning light in the face of the instrument which illuminates if either a chart (or two charts with a two-man instrument) is not in position or if recordings cease to be made because of a lack of pressure by the stylus on the chart.

The system used by both Jaeger and Veeder-Root is the provision of a window in the speedometer face through which the driver can see whether a chart is in position or whether proper recordings are being made.

Modern electronic tachographs such as the Kienzle 1318 type have in-built diagnostic facilities to provide continuous checks for system failures. In particular there is indication on the chart where power loss occurs as a result of disconnection of the voltage supply with the vehicle both moving and stationary. Similarly, failure of the impulse generator system as a result of malfunction in the impulse sender unit or in the connecting cable produces characteristic traces on the chart and failure of the mode recording system results in the red LED flashing repeatedly with the instrument front closed and both charts in their respective positions.

Engine Speed Recording

Some tachograph instruments have a facility for additionally recording engine speeds in revolutions per minute. Kienzle produces a combined road and engine speed tachograph model. These instruments incorporate a conventional rev-counter on the face along with the speedometer and an additional stylus which records, all the time the engine is running, the engine revolutions on the reverse side of special charts designed for use with this particular type of instrument. The

Figure 1.7   *Kienzle 1318 tachograph with engine speed indicator up to 3300 rpm*

recordings produced by these instruments can be read simultaneously with suitable analysis equipment so that engine speed can be compared to road speeds throughout a journey. It it useful also to indicate excessive engine-idle speed which is wasteful of fuel. Since it records engine speed continuously this facility allows for accurate monitoring of engine or power take-off performance. An engine speed warning light or audible signal contact is usually incorporated so that a predetermined maximum can be set to indicate to the driver if he revs the engine beyond the pre-set limit and if this engine speed is exceeded this is indicated on the chart by the position of the trace on the rpm recording field.

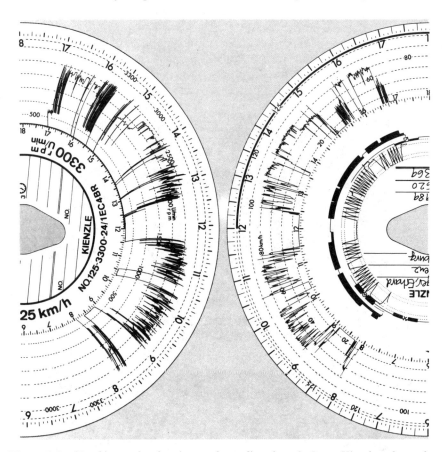

Figure 1.8   *Matching road and engine speed recordings from the Lucas Kienzle tachograph*

Intrinsically Safe Tachograph Systems

Vehicles carrying dangerous goods as defined under ADR (ie The European Agreement on the International Carriage of Dangerous Goods by Road) or under relevant British legislation on the carriage of hazardous goods must be fitted with a battery master cut-off switch in order to minimise dangers from an electrical discharge when the vehicle is standing in hazardous areas (ie areas where an explosive atmosphere could develop). Where tachographs are used to produce the driver's record, isolation of the battery would cause the electrically-driven clock to stop and result in an incomplete chart record. Additionally, the clock would need to be re-set each time the battery master switch was operated. Thus a way is needed to leave the clock working when the vehicle is in a hazardous area.

This type of electrical problem is not new to the oil and mining industries, and an engineering discipline has been developed to enable electricity to be used in areas where an explosive atmosphere may exist at any time. Intrinsically safe protection is defined in the UK at the Safety in Mines Research Establishment (SMRE) with approval and certification being dealt with by the British Approvals Service for Electrical Equipment in Flammable Atmospheres (BASEEFA). Similar standards certification systems exist in other European countries.

The basic requirement is that the energy available from the power source or sources with the equipment operating in the safe mode, must be insufficient to ignite the air-gas mixture even with two earth faults existing in the safety network and/or its protected circuit. In addition, each component must itself be intrinsically safe, so there is no danger of an accidental short circuit or earth within the component.

Lucas Kienzle Instruments Limited in the UK has obtained full BASEEFA certification for an intrinsically safe tachograph system for those vehicles carrying dangerous goods which are required to be fitted with a battery master switch in order to allow the tachograph clock to continue operating when the master switch is off. The system incorporates a barrier device to limit the current by-passing the battery master switch, a revised electronic circuit within the tachograph, so that the capacitors inherent in electronic clock operation do not feed power back into the vehicle wiring circuit and a minor modification to the battery master switch to enable it to meet the exacting BASEEFA specification.

Tachographs which met the BASEEFA requirements must carry a BASEEFA insignia either on a separate label or on its date plate and the battery master switch must be of an approved type.

2: Installation and Calibration of Tachographs

For tachographs to be fitted and used in goods and passenger vehicles as the legal means of record keeping it is necessary for the installation to be calibrated and sealed at approved workshops and by approved fitters in accordance with the specification set out in the technical annex to EC Regulation 3821/85 (see Appendix I). In the UK this function is carried out by Department of Transport approved tachograph centres (see Appendix VI for list of addresses).

Installation

Installation of tachographs is a task for skilled and trained fitters and the legal requirement, as shown in Appendix I, is for installation, repair and calibration to be carried out only by approved fitters and workshops (ie in the UK at DTp approved tachograph centres as mentioned above). It is important to recognise that the tachograph is a highly efficient and accurate recording instrument and as such its installation must be sound, secure and to within closely defined accuracy limits.

Tachographs are normally installed in new vehicles by vehicle manufacturers as original equipment (unless the operator specifies otherwise). In this case, the instrument is built into the vehicle dashboard and connected to the vehicle gearbox by means of a heavy duty drive cable (earlier mechanical-drive types) or an electric cable (electronic types). At this stage the installation is not calibrated or sealed (although the instrument head itself is calibrated and sealed at manufacture).

When instruments are fitted to vehicles retrospectively (which may only be legally carried out at approved workshops) this involves replacing the existing speedometer with a tachograph head or adding a remotely mounted tachograph instrument within the driver's line of vision while leaving the original speedometer in position. With some vehicles the existing dashboard will not accommodate a tachograph in which case a new dash panel is needed to accept the instrument. On certain vehicles when the tachograph replaces the speedometer it is sometimes necessary to provide replacement instruments for the fuel gauge and temperature gauge and replacement warning lights for the ignition, oil pressure and headlamp mainbeam where these were previously incorporated in the speedometer face as a composite instrument.

Note: The requirement for retro-fitting of tachographs as described above is now rare since most vehicles which require instruments for legal reasons have been fitted with them at the point of manufacture.

Dashboard Fitment

The instrument is normally mounted in the dashboard fascia with the face sloping away from the perpendicular at an angle of approximately 40 degrees but this angle may vary.

Routeing of Drive Cable

Location and routeing of the mechanical drive cable is critical to ensure that the radius of curves is adequate to allow proper rotation of the inner cable within the outer casing and consequently efficient and accurate operation of the instrument. The installation of cables with restricted radius curves results in strain and excessive friction between the inner cable and the outer casing causing the former eventually to overheat leading to premature failure of the drive. Additionally, cables must be located where they are protected from chafing by moving parts of the vehicles, vibration, heat (exhausts and radiators) accidental damage (where drivers cannot step on them when climbing on catwalks, etc,) interference during routine maintenance, dirt and water from road wheels and oil ingress from leaking components (engine, clutch, gearbox). With electronic instruments, routeing of the signal cable is not so critical (apart from ensuring it does not get trapped or that it does not come into contact with hot vehicle components or is contaminated by engine oil, fuel or other oils and greases). Sufficient spare cable can be coiled on the chassis to enable the vehicle gearbox to be pulled out for clutch repairs without seal breakage and thereby avoid a costly visit to an approved tachograph workshop for re-calibration and re-sealing.

Adaptor Gearbox for Cable Drive

Mechanical cable drives are connected to the vehicle gearbox through an adaptor or triplex gearbox. Where vehicles are fitted with two-speed rear axles, it is usual for the cable drive to be routed via a two-speed adaptor to ensure accuracy of recording when driving in either high or low rear-axle ratios. When necessary, due to the cable layout, the normal adaptor is replaced by an angle-drive adaptor. When it is desirable to retain the vehicle speedometer as well as fitting a tachograph, an adaptor is available to permit the driving of two cables from a single gearbox connection.

Connections for Electronic Instruments

Corrector gearboxes as described above are not required with electronic-type tachographs. A transducer or pulse generator unit is fitted to the vehicle gearbox and pulses or signals are transmitted by cable to the tachograph head. Calibration is carried out within the instrument by means of electronic circuitry. On Kienzle instruments a potentiometer adapts the tachograph to the vehicle's revs/km output. Calibration on earlier Veeder-Root instruments is by adjustment of the digital input to the microprocessor and on Jaeger instruments the electronic regulator processes the drive ratio.

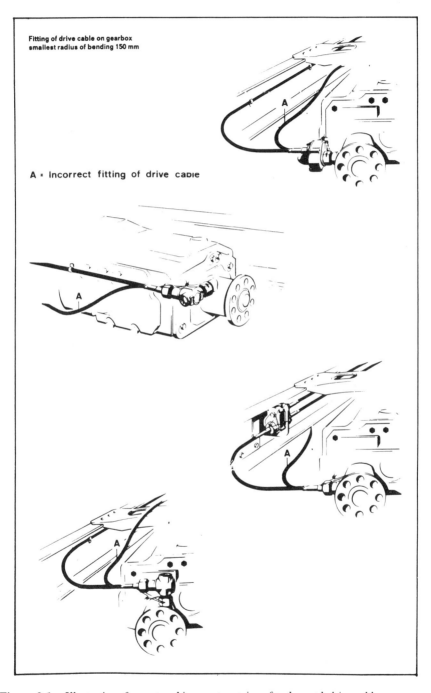

Fitting of drive cable on gearbox
smallest radius of bending 150 mm

A = Incorrect fitting of drive cable

Figure 2.1   *Illustration of correct and incorrect routeing of tachograph drive cables*

Calibration and Sealing

To ensure the accuracy of tachograph recordings it is necessary to have the installation tested and calibrated at an approved workshop (ie a DTp Tachograph Centre in the UK).

Calibration involves testing the instrument in the vehicle to ensure the accuracy of the clock and the recordings of distance and speed to within pre-defined limits. This is done by running the vehicle on a rolling road one of which is installed in all approved workshops (except possibly, those in very remote areas).

The maximum tolerances permitted for a tachograph instrument at the time of installation are as follows:

1. distance travelled: ±2 per cent
2. speed: ±4 kilometres per hour
3. time: ±2 minutes per day or 10 minutes per 7 days.

Wider 'in use' tolerances are permitted (see Appendix I) in order to allow for wear and tear on the vehicle (eg tyre wear and replacement).

When an approved workshop has established the accuracy of the recordings, having in some instances made the necessary adjustments to bring them within the maximum permitted tolerances and carried out any necessary repairs to ensure correct operation of the instrument, an approval plaque or certification will be fixed to or near the instrument and then the complete installation will be sealed so that any future interference with, or alteration to, the instrument or any parts of its drive mechanism can be readily detected.

The particular parts of the installation which are to be sealed are as follows:

1. The calibration plaque – this is either covered by transparent film which destroys the information on the plaque if the film is removed, or is contained in a sealed plastic cover.
2. Two ends of the mechanical drive cable between the instrument head and the vehicle gearbox and electronic cables linking the drive to the instrument head.
3. The adaptor gearbox which connects the drive to the vehicle gearbox.
4. Any intermediate connecting points.
5. The switch mechanism for vehicles with two or more rear drive-axle ratios.
6. The casings provided to protect the equipment from damp and dust and interference.

Figure 2.2 *Calibration plaque of Lucas Kienzle type which is fitted inside the instrument head. Details are completed at the time of installation*

These seals must remain intact if the instrument is to be used for making legally acceptable records of the driving, working, break and rest periods of commercial vehicle drivers. Should the seals be broken for any reason whatsoever, then while they remain broken legal records cannot be made. The seals must be remade at the approved workshop to enable the tachograph to effectively be used again for official record-keeping purposes.

Frequency of Calibration

Regulations specify the occasions and frequency with which testing, calibration and sealing must be carried out.

These are as follows:

1. Following initial and any subsequent installation of equipment.
2. After every repair to the tachograph installation or after the disturbance of the installation in connection with other repairs to the vehicle.
3. After any alteration to the installation or vehicle which may affect the accuracy of the indication or recording of speed or distance.
4. After any change of wheel or tyre size which affects the effective wheel circumference (replacement of worn tyres of the same size and of generally similar tread pattern are *not* reason for re-calibration).
5. Not later than six years from the date of the previous full calibration (as indicated by the date on the official installation plaque in or near the instrument head).

Normally, in the case of a broken cable when the seals are still intact, full re-calibration may not be necessary if a turns count indicates that the characteristic coefficient of the vehicle has not altered (see p 40). In such cases a 'minor work procedure' would be followed.

Calibration Checks

If the vehicle has not been back to an approved workshop in the meantime, no later than two years from the date of the original calibration the vehicle must be submitted to an approved workshop for a 'check' or periodic inspection. According to the EC Regulation (3821/85 Annex 1) the periodic inspection should take place with the equipment in situ. The particular points for inspection are:

1. the correct functioning of the equipment.
2. the state of the seals.
3. the characteristic coefficient of the vehicle.

Calibration Records

At the time of carrying out a test and calibration of a tachograph installation the approved workshop completes certain documents as follows:

1. The workshop's own records of inspections.
2. In the UK a DTp form GV212 (Register of Tachograph Installation Plaques Issued).
3. An installation plaque which is affixed near to or inside the instrument case.

When an installation has been previously calibrated, the old installation plaque must be removed and destroyed.

Information on the installation plaque is as follows:

(a) the name and address of the approved workshop or fitter
(b) the seal code of the workshop/fitter
(c) the date of the calibration test
(d) the following technical data:
  i characteristic coefficient 'w' of the vehicle expressed as:
$$w = \ldots\text{rev/km}$$
  or
$$w = \ldots\text{imp/km}$$
  ii effective circumference of the driving wheel tyres expressed as
  $1 = \ldots\text{mm.}$
(e) vehicle registration number.

See p 36 for illustration.

After fixing the installation plaque to the instrument, it is sealed in such a way that the information it shows is automatically destroyed if any attempt is made to remove the seal or the seal itself is destroyed.

Calibration Test

Before undertaking the test, the approved workshop must ensure that the vehicle meets certain requirements as follows:

1. It must be unladen (articulated tractive units should not be accompanied by a trailer) and in normal operating condition.
2. The tyres fitted to the vehicle must comply with legal requirements concerning the condition and maintenance of tyre equipment (in the UK, *The Road Vehicles (Construction and Use Regulations) 1986* Sections 24, 25 and 26).
3. The tyres should be inflated in accordance with manufacturer's recommendations.

When these items have been checked the test for mechanically-driven instruments is then commenced as follows:

1. The tachograph drive cable is removed from the output end adaptor gearbox (or a two-speed unit if fitted).
2. The drive cable is checked for excessive rotational resistance.
3. A tachograph instrument portable test drive unit is connected to the instrument using a suitable length of cable and adaptors in a way which enables both the tachograph and the driving unit speed display to be clearly read when sitting in the vehicle cab.
4. The instrument clock is checked to ascertain that it is working (ie that power is connected and it is set to the right time).
5. A chart is inserted into the tachograph in a 'time right' position after the following details have been entered on the face:

(a) chart identification (ie the words 'Test Chart')
(b) the tester's name.
(c) vehicle registration number.
(d) tachograph make and serial number
(e) date of the test
(f) distance recorder reading at the start of the test
(g) following the test further information is added to the chart:
    i Distance recorder reading at the end of the test.
    ii Total distance covered during the test.

6. The instrument face illumination is checked to ensure that the speed scale can be seen satisfactorily.
7. The portable driving unit is then switched on and the speed is progressively increased to full scale deflection on the tachograph speed scale (see below). At this point the speed indications on the tachograph instrument and on the driving unit are compared. The tachograph speed recording should be easily read and free from oscillation.
8. Next, the speed is decreased rapidly to zero to enable the motion of the speed stylus relative to the record sheet to be investigated. Rapid speed reductions such as this will show as radial lines on the chart.
9. The tester next selects three, equally spaced speeds which cover the speed range of the tachograph, preferably in multiples of 20kph because these are easier to read on the scale (say 40kph, 80kph and 120kph on a 125kph instrument). With the instrument run at these speeds a comparison is made between the speeds indicated on the tachograph instrument and on the driving unit and between the indicated speeds and the recorded speeds on the chart. Acceleration checks are also carried out to check appropriate recordings.
10. When checking the instrument and chart at the end of the above test, the tester will ensure that the speed pointer on the instrument returns to the correct rest point and the recording on the chart coincides with the base line of the speed recording area of the chart.
11. Further, the instrument will be checked to ensure that it will maintain a steady speed indication at a constant speed input from the driving unit and that the recording on the chart also shows a constant speed.
12. The stylus which records other activity modes (ie attendance at work and break and rest periods) is checked to ensure it is working and recording correctly.
13. While the instrument is being run for testing the speed recording, the distance recorder will also have been operating and a check is made to compare the distance shown on the instrument distance recorder with the distance recorded on the chart. This should be accurate to within one per cent.
14. The instrument clock is checked with a clock tester to ensure its accuracy within the permitted tolerances of time keeping, namely two minutes per day or 10 minutes per seven days.

Note: The instrument is removed from the vehicle for convenience while the above mentioned tests are carried out.

15. The characteristic coefficient of the vehicle tachograph (identified by the symbol 'w' on the calibration plaque) is measured by running the vehicle on a roller test rig (rolling road).
16. The effective circumference of the driving wheel tyres (identified by the symbol '1') is also measured on the roller test rig.
17. The installation is sealed (see below) and the installation plaque is completed and attached near to or inside the instrument (see under heading Calibration Records).
18. A final road test is carried out.

   Note: Certain of these processes differ when electronic drive instruments are undergoing calibration. In particular items 1 and 2 in the list will differ.

Repairs, Adjustments and Seals
In carrying out the calibration test as described above, any existing seals on the installation will be removed and necessary repairs and adjustments will be made to ensure the installation operates correctly and within the defined permitted tolerances.

Permitted Tolerances
The EC regulations specify permitted limits of accuracy for tachograph equipment as follows:

	During Bench Tests	*On Installation*	*In Use*
1. Speed	±3kph	±4kph	±6kph
2. Distance	±1 per cent	±2 per cent	±4 per cent
3. Time		±2 minutes per day	
		or ±10 minutes per seven days	

Sealing the Installation
Following testing and calibration of the tachograph, the whole installation is officially sealed so that any attempt to alter or tamper with it (or if the system is disconnected) will be easily detected. It should be noted that if any of the seals are broken accidentally or otherwise, it is no longer possible to make legally acceptable recordings for the purposes of the EC driver's hours and records regulations. The seals which are used must be marked on one side with the special indent allocated to the approved workshop. The other side may be blank or may have the tachograph manufacturer's trade mark impressed upon it.

   Information on the seal face shows:

1. A code indicating the country of sealing.
2. In the UK, followed by the code letter of the Traffic Area in which the centre is located as follows:

Northern A	South Wales G
Yorkshire B	Western H
North Western C	South Eastern K
West Midland D	Scottish North L
East Midland E	South Scottish M
Eastern F	Metropolitan N

3. The number allocated to the approved workshop by the competent authority of the member state (the Department of Transport in the UK). This number is issued in compliance with the EC regulations which specify that each member state must keep a central register of such marks.

The following parts of the tachograph installation are sealed:

1. The installation plaque – unless it is made in such a way that it cannot be removed without destroying the information printed on it.
2. The two ends of the link between the tachograph head and the vehicle (ie the ends of the drive cable or electric cable).
3. The adaptor gearbox and the point of its insertion into the vehicle drive train.
4. The two-speed corrector gearbox on vehicles with two-speed axles.
5. The links joining the adaptor and switch mechanism with the rest of the drive chain.
6. The castings protecting the internals of the tachograph head from misuse, dirt or damp.
7. Between any two parts of the installation which, if they were separated, would allow access to parts of the tachograph installation which affect its satisfactory operation.

Approved Workshops

Testing, calibration, repair and adjustment of tachograph installations must be carried out at approved workshops or by approved fitters (workshops and fitters in each EC member state are approved by the relevant authority – in the UK the DTp). These approved workshops are spread throughout the country, and lists of addresses are readily available (see Appendix VI for list of UK centres). Approved workshops are identified by a special sign which in the UK has white letters and symbols on a blue background.

Before workshops or fitters are approved they are inspected by the relevant authority (in the UK the DTp carries out this procedure) to ensure that the premises and equipment confirm to prescribed requirements.

A summary of these requirements is as follows:

1. **Premises:**
(a) they must have a potential for carrying out work on at least 2,000 vehicles per year (normally covered by having two work bays) except in remote areas;
(b) there must be off-road parking facilities for two vehicles with easy access into the work bays;
(c) the work bays must be capable of accepting vehicles up to 12 m long and 2.5m wide;
(d) there must be a pit, hoist or lift (not jacks);
(e) a clean area must be allocated for adaptor gearbox assembly and repair work and where the calibration equipment is kept;
(f) a steel lockable cupboard or safe must be provided for the storage of records, installation, plaques, plaque holders, sealing pliers and punches;

(g) there must be sufficient storage space for equipment and tachograph components.

2. Equipment:
(a) tachograph roller test rig for vehicle calibration (not required in remote area centres);
(b) Tachograph Portable Drive Test Unit;
(c) clock tester;
(d) optical tachograph chart analyser;
(e) sealing pliers and punches;
(f) tyre pressure gauge;
(g) compressor for inflating tyres;
(h) special tools as recommended by the tachograph manufacturer.

Testing of Equipment
The roller test rig, portable drive test unit and clock tester must be re-calibrated at least every six months to ensure their accuracy.

3. Staff:
Fitters carrying out tachograph work must hold a certificate of competence indicating that they have recorded the necessary training in installation, inspection, calibration and repair of the systems. This certificate is only valid for three years after which a refresher course must be taken.

3: Charts and Recordings

Charts

A specification for tachograph charts (referred to in the regulations as record sheets but more commonly called charts in the industry) is set out in Annex 1 of EC Regulation 3821/85 and all charts used for recording legal information relating to driving time must be of a type which conforms to this specification.

In the main, charts are exclusive to particular makes and models of tachograph instrument but there are universal charts now available which can be used in both standard and automatic-type tachographs. Operators should check carefully to ensure they issue drivers with the correct charts for the instruments to be used. Charts which meet the necessary requirements are sold at approved workshops and by a number of ancillary suppliers by mail order and through stationers' outlets.

Charts may be personalised by overprinting the operator's name and company logo if sufficient quantities are ordered and they may also be serially numbered on a voluntary basis if required but this is not a legal necessity. Tachograph charts conforming to the EC specification are marked with an 'e' approval mark and a code letter/digit representing the country of manufacture in addition to the manufacturer's name, trade name and address, the maximum speed measurement range of the chart in kilometres per hour (eg 125km/h) and the 'e' approval mark of the tachographs in which they may only be used.

Charts which do not bear these identifying marks are not acceptable for making statutory recordings. It is illegal both to use non-approved charts (or approved charts in instruments for which they are not approved) and for firms to have their own charts printed.

Legal Requirements for Charts
The legal requirements for tachograph charts set out in Annex 1 to 3821/85 are as follows:

General Points

1. They must be capable of showing recordings which are indelible, legible and clear.
2. There must be capacity on the charts for recording activities over a minimum period of 24 hours.
3. They must retain their dimensions under normal conditions of humidity.

4. It must be possible to write on them without damaging them and without affecting the legibility of the information entered by the driver in the centre field of the chart.
5. Under normal conditions of storage, the recordings on charts must remain clearly legible for at least one year.
6. The printed areas on charts must be accurate to provide precise time recordings. (There is some concern about charts which are not accurately printed and which produce inaccurate time recordings.)

Recording Areas and Graduation

1. Specific recording areas must be provided on charts as follows:
   (a) an area exclusively reserved for recording speed;
   (b) an area exclusively reserved for recording distance travelled;
   (c) one or more areas for recording:
       i driving time,
       ii other periods of work and attendance at work,
       iii breaks from work,
       iv rest periods.
2. The chart must have a time scale around the whole area of the chart graduated principally into 15-minute intervals and secondly into 5-minute intervals.
3. The area for recording speed must be scaled in divisions of 20km/h or less and the speed for each marking must be shown in figures against that marking. The symbol 'km/h' must be shown at least once in the speed recording area. The last marking on the scale must coincide with the upper limit of the range of measurement.
4. The area for recording distance travelled must be set out so that the recording of the distance travelled in kilometres can be read without difficulty.
5. The area designated for recording the amount of time spent in carrying out different activities (driving, work and break periods) must be marked so it is easy to distinguish clearly between the various periods of time.

Space for Handwritten Entries
The centre field (area) of the chart must be designed to enable crew members to write in at least the following details:

1. Their surname and first name.
2. The date and place where the activities to be recorded on the sheet begin and the date and place where the activities end.
3. The registration number of the vehicle to be driven (and the numbers of other vehicles if more than one is driven during the time when the chart is in use).
4. The distance recorded (odometer) readings of the vehicle (or vehicles) in which the chart is used (ie to start and finish reading and, by subtraction, the total distance covered).
5. The time when any change of vehicle takes place.

Structure of Charts

Tachograph charts are made of pressure sensitive coated paper. The scale graduations and other information on the face of the chart is printed and shows clearly distinguishable markings against which recordings are made and can be checked. In the centre of the chart is a hole specially shaped to make a close fit on the chart mounting pillar in the instrument. Each of the major tachograph manufacturers has a different design of pillar and fitting arrangement and, consequently, the centre hole profile in charts differs from one make to another.

For this reason, operators will find considerable advantage in standardising on one make of tachograph, not only to avoid the problems of administering a system involving the use of two or even three makes of instrument, but also to save drivers the problem of using more than one chart a day when they drive more than one vehicle.

The purpose of these precisely shaped centre holes is to ensure that the chart can be inserted in the instrument only in a 'time right' manner, and then, subsequently, recordings will be accurate in relationship to time throughout the recording period. When the face of the instrument is closed with a chart in position the recording styli press on the face of the chart and as the chart revolves with the rotation of the clock each stylus engraves a fine trace. This exposes the backing paper (coloured black) to produce a series of recordings on each of the three principal recording areas of the chart.

On some charts the reverse side is printed with markings to enable the driver to make manual recordings in the event of instrument failure or in other circumstances where the instrument cannot make recordings for him. This side of the chart is not pressure sensitive (except in the case of those special instruments that additionally record engine speed, in which case the reverse side of the chart has graduations against which engine revolutions per minute are recorded on a pressure sensitive surface). Charts, both before and after use, are susceptible to unintentional marking and therefore care is needed in handling them and storing them so as to avoid soiling or damage of the recording areas and possible destruction of legal recordings.

Recordings

The process of recording on tachograph charts involves a number of simultaneous actions by the respective instrument styli. With a chart in the instrument and the clock set to the right time and functioning correctly, each stylus engraves a fine trace in the appropriate recording area on the face of the chart.

Standard-Type Instruments
First, the speed stylus makes its trace on the base line of the speed recording area and continues to do so until the vehicle begins to move. Secondly, the distance stylus makes a simultaneous trace in the distance recording area. The precise location of the continuous distance trace within the recording area is determined by the position in which the stylus came to rest when the vehicle last stopped. The

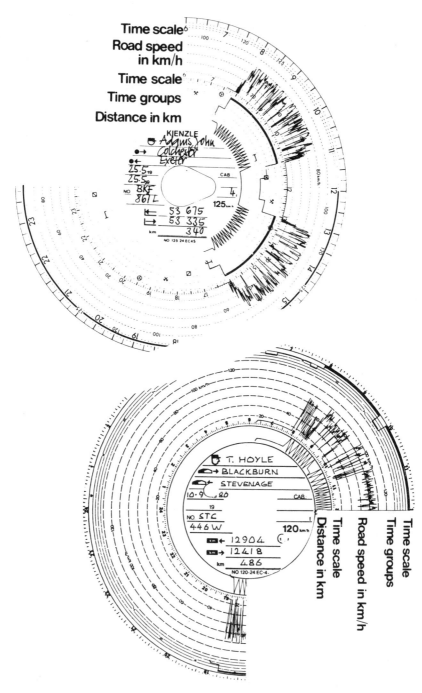

Figure 3.1   *Chart recording areas (a) Lucas Kienzle Standard type (b) Veeder-Root type*

stylus moves up and down to produce its recording of distance travelled only when the vehicle moves. Thirdly, the activity mode stylus makes a fine continuous trace within the marked area on the chart according to the position in which the driver activity mode switch on the top of the instrument is placed namely, driving, attendance at work, break or rest period.

When the vehicle starts to move each stylus begins to make its characteristic trace. The activity mode stylus is mechanically agitated (it is not vibrated) inside the instrument by a cam drive through the vehicle drive-line system and produces a broad running line, clearly distinguishable on the chart so there can be no doubt at all about when the vehicle was stationary and when it was moving. Differences in speed do not affect this recording and the very lowest of travel speeds will still result in a clear 'movement' trace. Contrary to certain impressions, engine tick-over does not produce a vibrationary running trace with EC tachographs.

Should the driver fail to select the correct activity position on the mode switch, a running trace will nevertheless be produced but this will appear on the chart in the recording area appropriate to the activity that the switch is indicating (ie in the

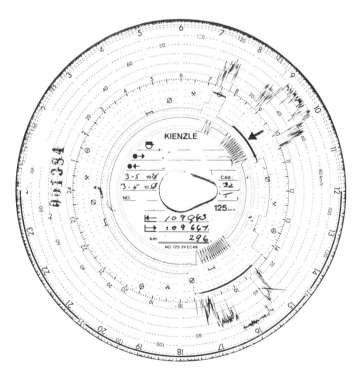

Figure 3.2 *Driving with the activity mode switch in the wrong position still produces a running trace but in the wrong place . . . in this case against break period*

'attendance at work' or 'break' areas) on most instruments. An omission such as this on the part of the driver is an offence. For this reason, it is important that the driver does remember to operate the switch because in different circumstances false recordings such as these can prove misleading and even make it appear that an operation was illegal. For example, if a driver stops to make a delivery and remembers to turn his switch to 'attendance at work' this will produce a correct recording. If he then decides to take a break immediately after making the delivery and without getting back into the cab (ie he goes into the firm's canteen where he is delivering or to a nearby cafe) he will have failed to turn the switch to 'break'. When he returns to his vehicle and drives away it will be too late to retrospectively record that a break was taken and the trace on the chart will show that the whole period between the two spells of driving was spent in attendance at work. In this situation, the driver should have taken the chart with him and manually recorded the appropriate activities and times.

Besides the activity mode stylus making its recording, the speed stylus moves upwards and makes a trace on the chart appropriate to the varying speeds at which the vehicle travelled. This trace will fluctuate up and down as the vehicle progressively slows and accelerates. It will show the maximum speed achieved and period of continuous driving at steady speeds as well as more erratic driving patterns characterised by indications of fierce acceleration and braking.

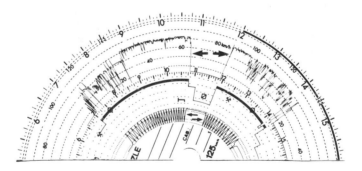

Figure 3.3   *Speed and distance recordings as described below*

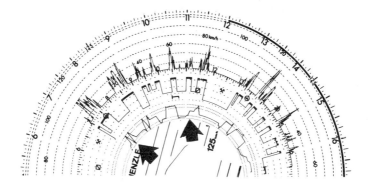

Figure 3.4 *Fast and slow speed recordings as indicated by the distance trace*

While the speed stylus is making its trace, the distance stylus moves up and down on the appropriate recording area of the chart but over a limited path with one full upward or downward stroke representing each full five kilometres travelled by the vehicle. At low speed the angles between the upward and downward strokes is increased while at high speed the trace closes up and the angles between the strokes reduce sharply.

Automatic-Type Instruments
The Kienzle Automatic tachograph produces a time trace which differs from that made by the standard type of instrument previously described. In this case, the time recording is made on a single circumference round the chart with the driving trace occurring whenever the vehicle moves forward and the other traces relating to work and breaks occurring when the vehicle comes to rest with the activity mode switch turned to one of the relative positions. Recorded activities are differentiated by the relative widths of the traces. Driving is indicated by the broadest trace, crossed hammers activity by a narrower trace, attendance at work by an even narrower trace and break and rest periods by a single line. For defining the activity recordings on the charts, the respective widths of the traces are pre-printed on blank charts to use as a key.

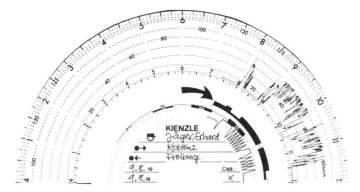

Figure 3.5 *Lucas Kienzle Automatic Tachograph type recording as described above,
showing the single time group trace arrowed*

Fourth-Stylus Recordings

Certain versions of tachograph instruments can accommodate the inclusion of a
fourth recording stylus for ancillary purposes. This stylus can be connected electrically to any single item of vehicle mounted equipment to enable a monitoring
recording to be made on the chart, via sensors and a signal wire, every time that
particular piece of equipment is activated. Typical examples of the most popular
use of this facility are with fuel monitoring devices (see page 149), engine speed
recording, lorry-mounted cranes, discharge blowers or cargo pumps, tail-lifts, re-
frigeration motors or body temperature gauges to monitor temperature rises with
door openings, roller shutters or other vehicle doors. On emergency vehicles connection can be made to sirens, gongs or flashing lights to monitor the frequency
and duration of their use.

Protection of Charts

After use, care should be taken in handling and storing charts because they are
easily damaged and recordings may be accidentally defaced making analysis difficult or even impossible and, most importantly, removing legally required information. Damage can be caused by scratching with finger nails and any other sharp
object, by standing heavy items on the chart, by folding and putting it in a pocket
and by clipping it with paper clips or bulldog clips plus a variety of other practices. Similarly, oil, coffee, tea, water and many other liquid and greasy sub-
stances will have a deteriorating effect on charts. Bearing in mind the legal
requirements to keep charts available for inspection for 12 months after use, it is
essential to ensure that drivers realise what causes damage and that they are aware
of the legal need to protect charts. Ideally, they should be provided with some
form of wallet or protective case or pouch for this purpose.

In the office, charts should be stored so that they are not mixed with other
heavy objects stood upon them. An ideal method of storage is on pegs on a wallboard or in a cabinet where charts for each driver or vehicle can be clearly and separately stored with safety. Suitable aids to safe storage are readily available from
most tachograph chart suppliers.

4: Chart Filing and Storage Systems

Since the introduction of legislation in the UK requiring the mandatory fitment and use of tachographs, as there has been a proliferation of chart analysis aids so has there been a proliferation of storage, filing and protective systems for charts. Many firms joined the rush to cash in on this lucrative market brought about very much by the vunerability of tachograph charts. They easily become dirtied and damaged and thus are merely wasted – if they have not been used – or they are legal documents which have become defaced and this is an offence.

It is an important aspect of the EC regulations, firstly, that drivers must keep charts clean and free from damage both before and after use and, secondly, that employers must retain charts for 12 months after receiving them back from the driver after use. During this period, inspection of the charts may be requested by the enforcement authorities so they must be readily available and identifiable either by driver's name or by vehicle registration number.

Choice as to which of these alternative methods is preferable for filing purposes is left to the operator. Much depends on whether drivers regularly keep to one vehicle – which simplifies matters considerably -or whether a driver may change between a number of vehicles during the day in which case his chart will feature a number of different vehicle registration numbers. The important point is that, so long as the charts required by the enforcement authorities (whether requested by driver's name or by vehicle registration number) can be readily produced there will be no difficulty.

Generally, on a routine inspection, the enforcement authorities will accept charts filed by either means, vehicle or driver, but if they are following up from a silent roadside check it is likely that they will request charts by vehicle registration number for a specified period of time. In this case, there will be no difficulty if charts are filed in driver sequence, so long as the necessary charts relating to all driving of the vehicle during the period in question can be produced by cross referencing to traffic sheets or other documentation which shows who was driving the vehicle on each day.

Supply firms were quick to realise that there would be a need for suitable cases, pouches and wallets to enable drivers to keep charts protected and for filing and storage systems for the employer to keep charts properly stored. Thus a whole range of products have come on to the UK market both from the tachograph manufacturers themselves and from ancillary supplies manufacturers (see Appendix VII).

Despite the wide choice of proprietary storage and filing equipment available, many vehicle operators have adopted or manufactured their own storage systems ranging from high quality cabinet work with dowelling pegs to simple pegs on a wallboard or even nails in the wall.

One of the essential aspects of any storage system is that it must be simple to operate initially and remain so in the long term. One of the dangers of sophisticated and complex storage systems is that they could prove unworkable in the long term when urgently or specially needed charts of a month or three months ago cannot be found in the right place. Any system is dependent on very accurate filing and while this is available all is well, but as soon as the quality or the concentration of the person doing the filing fails the whole system becomes defunct.

What is important to remember is the reason why charts are being stored. There is no legal requirement for expensive or sophisticated storage or filing systems, merely an ability to locate particular charts quickly if required and make them available on request by the enforcement authorities.

5: Chart Analysis Equipment – Manual and Electronic

Examination of tachograph chart recordings with the naked eye and without any measuring scale is both laborious and inaccurate. At best, the examiner can make an approximate assessment of the times relevant to legal limitations driving, other work, break and rest periods and a calculation of distance covered. However, if many charts are to be examined (remember, a driver will normally produce at least five per week) the ability and interest of the examiner will decline rapidly with a consequent reduction in efficiency and accuracy.

To combat this difficulty a variety of analysis equipment has become available. This ranges from simple hand-held analysis discs costing very little money to sophisticated electronic analysers and then to computers costing large sums which will produce whole fleet records and cost analyses from input data and from electronic scanning of charts.

In this chapter a variety of analysis equipment is described but it is important to note that new devices occasionally appear on the market as firms see the potential opportunities in the chart reading business. At the time of going to press there are a number of prototype devices which may or may not eventually become marketable products.

Driver Analysis Equipment

At its most basic level, the need for checking tachograph charts exists with the driver who has a duty to ensure that he does not exceed the legal limits on his driving hours and working time and has had his correct break and rest periods. Many drivers will keep a running total of these times in their heads and in any case, most will know that their daily working schedules are well within legal limits so they will not be worried. However, for drivers who are likely to operate right up to the limits – and need to do so to satisfy operating schedules and achieve maximum driving and working efficiency, there is a clear need for them to be able to calculate what hours they have worked and driven and how much more time they have left available to continue before they exceed their limits. To expect them to do so from a visual inspection of the chart is not satisfactory and could lead to a situation where they are tempted to stop short of their destination to be on the 'safe side' – perhaps a vital 20 minutes or 30 minutes short which could have enabled the driver to get the vehicle back to base to be reloaded or used again, and saved the cost of a night-out allowance.

Cheap and simple devices to enable the driver to calculate times worked against

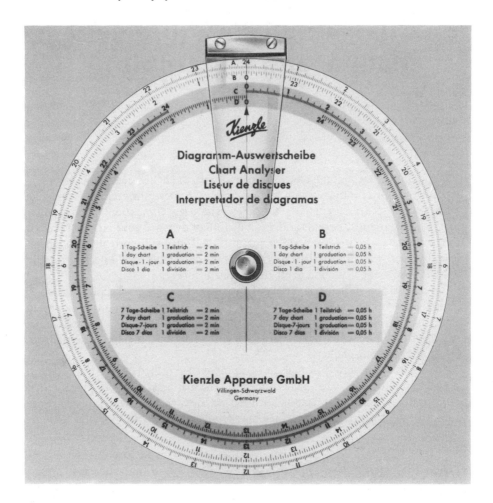

Figure 5.1   *Chart analysis disc*

permissible limits are readily available. One example comprises a plastic circular disc with a 24-hour time scale marked off with the legal limits on driving and duty times. With the aid of a rotating cursor the driver can measure the accumulated time and the time left available for driving within the daily limit.

Management Analysis Equipment

Since the EC regulations demand that employers make periodic inspection of charts, management and supervisory staffs have a specific need to ensure that drivers have complied with the driving hours law in all its various aspects and therefore will need a facility which enables them to do this quickly and accurately. More sophisticated types of measuring disc are marketed for this purpose by, for example, Kienzle and by other suppliers. The Kienzle chart analysis disc is made of plastic and is approximately 160mm in diameter with a series of printed time scales on the face. It has four time scales; the outer one (A scale) is a 24-hour scale marked *clockwise* round the outer edge and graduated in two-minute time intervals; the next, inner, time scale (B scale) is graduated in three-minute time intervals and goes *anti-clockwise* round the disc. Two further scales are provided for analysis of charts from the Kienzle mini tachograph. These C and D scales are also usable for seven-day chart packs and the time scale on the disc provides for 26-hour rotation. They are marked in two-minute graduations on the *clockwise* scale and three minutes on an *anti-clockwise* scale.

A clear plastic lip, mounted from the rear of the disc on the central spindle can be revolved round the disc with finger pressure. Within the plastic lip is a hairline cursor which is used to define the beginning and end of activity periods on the chart against the time scale on the outer edge of the disc (see illustration of working method on p 68).

Magnifiers

One of the principal difficulties encountered in reading tachograph chart recordings is the relatively small and detailed nature of the traces on the chart. Most people find difficulty in making a precise observation of recordings with the naked eye and if confronted with the need to examine either a small number of charts in great detail or a large number in lesser detail but within a limited period of time, the task becomes a burden, proving a great strain on the eyes. Consequently the efficiency and speed with which charts can be examined rapidly diminishes and the ultimate objective of accurate checking for errors, omissions and, more particularly, irregularities is defeated.

To overcome this problem magnifying equipment has been developed. Among these is the Kienzle Optical Analyser which comprises a frame on which is mounted a 2x magnifying lens above the chart table which accommodates the plastic chart analysis disc previously described. A bulb incorporated in the body of the analyser casts a light down on to the chart table so both magnification and illumination are provided to assist the chart analyst.

Besides this instrument which is designed specifically for use with tachographs, a simple, powerful magnifying lens can be useful to look at sections of the chart in greater scale. These are available from most opticians and illuminated 'map readers' are also available from specialist suppliers.

Greater Magnification

In certain instances there can be special interest in examining areas of chart recordings in much greater detail, when irregularities are suspected for example, or there appear to be discrepancies in the recordings. Normally, an optical analyser of the type described above will provide all the magnification necessary but in the special circumstances suggested an additional facility such as that provided by an occular attachment is useful. Such a device (available from Kienzle) fits on top of the optical analyser and increases the magnification to some 10x. Its principal shortcoming is that it provides a very limited field of vision so only one trace on

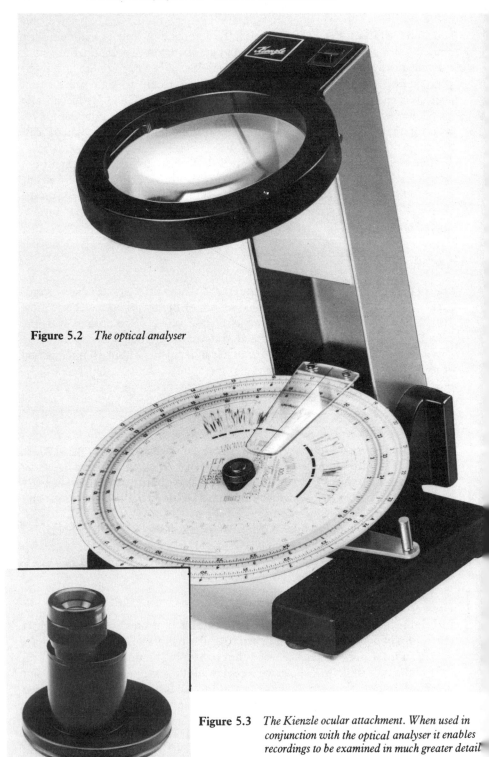

Figure 5.2   *The optical analyser*

Figure 5.3   *The Kienzle ocular attachment. When used in conjunction with the optical analyser it enables recordings to be examined in much greater detail*

the chart can be examined at a time. However, with this level of magnification very clear indication will be obtained of the most minor of discrepancies in recordings, particularly, instances of the instrument face being opened no matter how momentarily.

Although not a cheap item to buy, its cost can be more than justified if through its use irregular and illegal recordings can be eliminated. Only a few unnecessary payments of night-out allowance need be stopped to cover the cost and it is for this and similar purposes that the ocular attachment will be found most useful.

Mirror Analyser

A further accessory which is available is a mirror analyser for attachment to the optical analyser for use when an engine-speed recording tachograph has been used and a comparison is required between the simultaneous recordings of vehicle road speed and engine revolutions which appear on either side of the chart. The double-sided chart which is used in these instruments is placed on the mirror analyser and the engine revolutions per minute recording appears in the mirror above the road speed recording giving direct comparison and precise timing of both sets of recording. Thus any discrepancy between one and the other readily shows up and it would indicate abuse of the vehicle by over-revving or under-revving the engine in relationship to road speeds (eg allowing the engine to 'lug' or allowing the engine to idle for long periods), through misuse of the gearbox; driving slowly at high engine revs or revving the engine hard while stationary. Running the vehicle out of gear, which is a dangerous and illegal practice, can also be readily detected with this type of dual recording.

Figure 5.4   *The Kienzle optical analyser with mirror attachment for examining engine speed recording charts*

Electronic Analysers

The equipment described so far is quite inexpensive to buy, is basic in concept and simple to operate for analysing small numbers of charts. However, when the number of charts to be analysed increases, the need arises for a more sophisticated and more rapid means of analysis. For this reason manufacturers have developed electronic means of chart analysis; most notably, Veeder-Root with its ACE series of analysers and Lucas Kienzle with its M-FOS (Fleet Organisation System) model. Apart from the Lucas Kienzle computerised chart reader which will be dealt with later, these are the principal electronic analysers currently on the market.

Veeder-Root ACE Series Analysers

The Veeder-Root ACE series of analysers comprises three models – ACE 1, ACE 2, ACE 3. The analysers are based on a microprocessor and permit rapid conversion of the information from a tachograph chart to a digital format for electronic display on the machine.

The ACE machine is smaller and lighter than an office typewriter and is simple to use. With all models the method of operation is the same. A chart is placed on the chart table where it is secured by a magnetic cap and this is rotated electrically when the appropriate key is pressed. A magnifying lens and a light source directed on to the chart, aid the operator's vision. The instrument keyboard has a series of numbered keys 0-9 plus specific keys to input data relating to the vehicle, driver and work activity (ie the keys have the familiar activity mode symbols printed on them).

By rotation of the chart and operation of the keyboard, the operator can quickly analyse recorded activity each aspect of which is shown in numerical form on the digital display.

ACE 1 is a basic machine for use with a hand-written analysis form which has the facility to analyse the following data:

- Date
- Driver
- Vehicle
- Starting time
- Driving time
- Other Work Time

- Rest time
- Longest unbroken period of driving
- Total work time
- Total time from start to finish of day
- Distance Travelled

Data from other sources can be added to the manual analysis sheet as required.

ACE 2 has all the features of ACE 1 but one extra item of data can be added through the 'F1' entry key. This can be any item identifiable by a code of up to four digits. For example, fuel drawings, tons carried, number of loads or even a trailer code may be useful items to be recorded with this facility. Additionally, ACE 2 has an inbuilt printer which produces the analysed data in tally-roll form. This saves hand-written analysis and provides a simple 'written' record of the analysis of each chart.

ACE 3 goes a stage further than ACE 2 in that it has a data output point for

Figure 5.5   *Lucas Kienzle Optical Analyser with Mirror Attachment for examining engine speed recording charts*

direct connection to a data store or computer. This could be a tape cassette unit, a modem unit or directly into an existing computer network. To overcome the usual problems of hardware interface, an auxiliary tape cassette unit is available which can be interfaced with the most well-known types of computer.

Lucas-Kienzle M/FOS Analysers

The M/FOS analyser is a highly accurate and flexible desk-top analyser ideal for use at vehicle operating terminals where on-the-spot analysis of charts is required. The machine is microprocessor-based and is accurate to within 30 seconds on a 24-hour chart. A printer is available if required to give a tally-roll tape print-out of analysed data. Other features include 2x magnification of the chart, adjustable viewing angle and manual rotation of the chart. The keyboard contains keys for digits, EC-type activity mode symbols plus a facility to input fuel consumed. In most other respects this machine is similar to the Veeder-Root ACE machines already described.

6: Computerised Chart Analysis

Considerable attention has been given to the application of computers to tachograph chart analysis, some of it unfortunately misguided in that unsuspecting fleet operators have been given the impression that charts can be simply slotted into a computer which will read them automatically. With limited exceptions, computers do not read charts, they merely analyse data fed into them from other chart reading sources – manual or electronic – all of which require a high degree of manual intervention.

Operators are faced with a basic choice if they wish to proceed into the realms of computer analysis of chart data. Either they invest in the equipment (ie hardware and software) themselves which involves capital expenditure starting in the region of a few hundred pounds sterling and extending well up into five, or in the extreme, six figure sums or they can use the services of bureau firms of which there are quite a large number offering packages specifically related to tachograph use. In either case, it will be seen that, mainly, available systems are based on initial chart reading with manual or electronic equipment, as already described in earlier chapters, with subsequent input into a computer system to produce the resulting print-out of analysed data.

However, computers are being increasingly employed in conjunction with chart analysis systems to provide fleet operators with regular summaries of vehicle and driver activities and useful data on which decisions can be taken to help improve the economy or efficiency of driver activities and vehicle operations. Generally, all the computer systems currently being marketed are based on the latest micro hardware, some of which has become immensely popular and whose names are widely recognised. These systems are mostly IBM compatible. There are a number of other micro systems available which are known to be in use as part of tachograph chart analysis systems.

Besides these systems, Kienzle has its Auto/FOS system. This is a totally integrated computerised tachograph chart scanning and analysis system unlike the other systems mentioned above which are merely combination packages of electronic analysers and microcomputers. There are also the latest variants of desktop optical readers.

Lucas Kienzle FOS Computer System

This system is essentially a 'complete' system so far as computerised chart analysis is concerned because it does offer the operator a genuine chart reading facility.

This is achieved by automatic opto-electronic scanning of the tachograph chart and electronic data processing with the latest microprocessor control techniques. One essential aspect of the computer is that it is capable of use only with the Kienzle EC automatic tachograph which produces a different type of chart to other standard tachographs. The chart is characterised by the time group recording method which is based on a single circumferential trace round the chart with lines of differing thickness denoting the various activity modes of the driver.

The modular construction of the information centre facilitates perfect matching of configuration and storage location to meet specific operations and special needs for information. A choice is available between floppy disk or solid disk for data storage. Sufficient flexibility is built into the system to accommodate subsequent changes in the fleet.

The centre comprises a number of units such as the central processor, VDU optical reader and printer in a compact system. The system will also accommodate a variety of additional features or facilities, such as second disk drive. At the heart of this system is the Kienzle micro computer which can also be used for normal functional activities such as payroll, sales and purchase ledger, accounting, invoicing and stock control. Equally important is the opto-electronic scanner which, during an eight-second scan of the individual chart, breaks the face down into nearly 1,440,000 dots whose particular pattern is then turned into a data map of extreme accuracy. Kienzle has a range of software available to accompany the hardware.

A basic program is offered together with a number of optional programs depending on the requirements of the fleet user. For many operators the basic program will satisfy their needs. This comprises an analysis oriented to the vehicle and to the driver. Besides the detailed analysis of the time-related

Figure 6.1 *Lucas Kienzle M-FOS chart analysis sytem*

activities of both the vehicle and driver, the program includes the most important performance ratios as calculated from the contents of the charts.

Examples of those ratios are as follows:

Vehicle Performance
1. Driving time/kilometres
2. Driving time/duty time
3. Kilometres/driving time
4. Kilometres/duty time
5. Utilisation/day

Driver Performance
1. Kilometres/Driving time
2. Kilometres/number of stops
3. Duration of stops/number of stops
4. Driving time/waiting time/delivery time

Vehicle Analysis
The first part of the basic program allows a daily analysis of a vehicle's performance over a selected period – say one month. This can be supplemented by weekly sub-totals. Under some 56 headings both vehicle and driver-oriented information can be provided with individual columns allocated.

The second part of the basic program provides an overview of vehicle data by means of bar graphs which show clearly any deviation of daily activities from monthly averages. Part of the program provides a comprehensive summary of the performance of each vehicle in the fleet. It also includes monthly totals and averages for the entire fleet. The performance of each individual vehicle is measured against the fleet using the bar graph system.

Driver Analysis
Subsequent parts switch the emphasis from the vehicle to the driver and similar bar graph illustrations of driver performance are provided. Further parts of the program relate to crew analysis showing a summary of the cumulative performance of all personnel over a period and a bar graph illustration of the cumulative performance of drivers. This was written by Lucas Kienzle exclusively for UK Department of Transport use in its enforcement branches at the Traffic Area offices.

Gate Micro Systems

Gate Micro Systems in conjunction with Veeder-Root have developed the necessary computer software to receive and store information from the Veeder-Root ACE analyser via a low cost Commodore microcomputer.

Three important software programs are offered:

Program 1 provides system set up which enables the number of vehicles and drivers to be defined and the number of charts to be analysed, chart input date directly from the ACE 3 unit; and chart analysis which provides data by vehicle or driver on a daily or weekly basis. The data provided is as follows:

- Date
- Driver
- Vehicle
- Start time
- Finish time
- Driving time
- Other work time

- Total work time
- Total start-to-finished time
- Total distance
- Closing odometer reading
- Average speed
- Average fuel consumption
- Rest time

Program 2 gives a full check on compliance with the drivers' hours law with the following information displayed on the screen or printed out as hard copy.

- Details of infringements on one, more or all of the day's charts
- Details of any infringements by any driver over any period
- Details of the last seven or fourteen rolling days with cumulative totals.

Program 3 which is not currently available will combine chart data with data from other sources to provide a complete vehicle management system. 'Comprehensive costing data from detailed reports will enable fleets to be run in the most efficient and cost-effective way' according to the company.

By using the popular Commodore Pet computer system a wide variety of additional functions can be performed with the total system such as:

- Word processing
- Stock control
- Payroll

- Financial planning
- Results forecasting

Four major business-related software programs are available for use with the Commodore system to cover most application requirements.

Carmichael System

Based on the Memory System 7000 microcomputer system Carmichael and Sons offer two vital alternatives to fleet operators: the installation of their own system or the use of a chart reading and reporting system.

For companies who wish to control their own operation a complete package of both hardware and supporting software can be provided. The hardware comprises an electronic tachograph chart analyser and a Memory microcomputer and printer. The supporting software programs enable management to quickly check on drivers' hours infringements on a daily or weekly basis. Further programs can be supplied to cover:

- Vehicle control
- Stock control
- Payroll
- Sales/purchase/nominal ledgers
- Word processing

The chart reading service is based on a fast, efficient reading of charts with a 48-hour turnround. The analysis reports include details of:

- Date
- Driver
- Vehicle
- Classification
- Night out
- Closing odometer reading
- Total time

- Total duty
- Longest duty
- Longest driving
- Total driving
- Passive work
- Active work
- Rest

Up to five functions are available for extra data analysis such as fuel, route codes, customer codes and so on.

Other Systems

At the time of preparing this book the writer is aware of a number of further systems in which computer equipment is being used in connection with chart analysis services. The Freight Transport Association offers a chart reading bureau service for its members. Similarly Freight Computer Services is advertising a chart analysis service as part of its total package for the transport industry.

A word of caution is appropriate here. It is important that fleet operators should recognise that while many of the non-transport specialist bureau advertising chart analysis services fully understand all the ins and outs of the computer business they generally know very little about transport operations and even less about the application of the complex and restrictive legislation, and especially the drivers' hours law requirements, under which the industry operates. Thus the fleet operator needs to safeguard his legal position and not fall into the trap of being attracted by a 'super' computer system which at the end of the day tells him no more than he could have learned from a simple optical device at much less cost and without being deprived of his drivers' charts for a period of time.

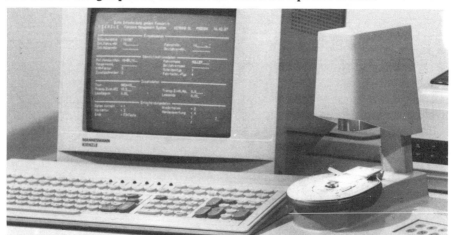

Figure 6.2   *Another desk-top computerised chart analysis system*

7: Checking Charts for Legal Purposes

Vehicle operators (both goods and passenger) are required by law to ensure that, where appropriate, drivers must keep records of their driving and working times, break and rest periods. Furthermore, there is a clear legal obligation for these records to be periodically checked by the employer under EC Regulation 3820/85 to ensure that the various aspects of the law have been complied with.

For a start, one of the conditions on which a goods or passenger vehicle operator's licence is granted in the UK is that the applicant promises by way of making a statutory declaration of intent that the law relating to drivers' hours and record keeping would be adhered to. Failure to comply can result in risk of loss of the licence. Similarly, in Europe, compliance with the EC drivers' hours law and tachograph requirements is, broadly, part of the 'good repute' requirement for starting in the transport business. Failure by European-based operators to comply can lead to penalties.

There are responsibilities on both the driver and the employer under both EC regulations and, quite separately, to UK employers and drivers under British regulations, to ensure that used tachograph charts are returned to the employer for safe keeping – in the case of the UK this must happen within 21 days.

EC Regulation 3821/85 (Articles 13 to 16) set out in detail the requirements for the use of the tachograph by the driver, including the need to ensure that the equipment functions correctly and continuously, and the driver's responsibilities in terms of completing the chart centre field and using the tachograph to record activities correctly. Article 16(2) specifically requires the driver to make manual entries if the tachograph is defective. Finally, drivers are required to comply with the requirements regarding driving hours, working times and break and rest periods specified in EC Regulation 3820/85.

The regulations make it clear that tachograph charts must be checked by the employer when they are returned to him by the driver. The purpose of checking is to ensure, in general terms, that legal requirements regarding the return of charts, their correct completion and correct observance of the driving hours rules are met. Therefore, a systematic check of all these items should be made in the following manner, after observing two vital points:

1. That drivers submit a chart for every day on which a relevant vehicle was driven within the scope of the regulations.
2. That charts are returned by the driver as required by law after retaining them for a specified period in case they are requested for inspection by an authorised

inspection officer. The driver, on request by such a person, must be able to produce charts relating to the current fixed week and the last day of the previous week in which he drove. UK drivers are required to return used charts no later than 21 days after use (see p 134).

Visual Check

Having obtained the used chart from the driver a visual check should be made of the following items:

1. If numbered charts are being used on a voluntary basis, that the chart carries a number which corresponds with numbered charts issued to the driver.
2. That the driver has entered:
    (a) his name (surname and christian name)
    (b) the date on which entries on the chart are first made
    (c) the date on which entries on the chart are last made (ie to cover the driver who uses that chart for a night shift operation crossing over midnight from one day into the next);
    (d) the place where use of the chart begins;
    (e) the place where use of the chart ends;
    (f) the registration number of the vehicle driven (if more than one vehicle is driven, the registration numbers of the other vehicles and the time of the changeover from one to another);
    (g) the distance recorder (odometer) reading at the beginning and end of the shift and by subtraction the total distance covered (in kilometres). Again, if more than one vehicle is driven, the distance recorder readings for the other vehicles should be shown.

Examination of Recordings

When these items have been verified, the actual recordings themselves should be examined. Ideally this would be done with an optical analyser (see p 55) for ease of reading but the task can be accomplished with the aid of a simple and inexpensive, plastic chart analysis disc (see p 54).

The chart analysis disc comprises a back plate marked with a clockwise time scale graduated in two-minute time intervals and an anti-clockwise scale graduated in three-minute time intervals and a clear plastic lip, fixed to the centre of the chart, which contains a hairline cursor.

Analyse the chart in the following manner:

1. Move the cursor round to the zero mark on the time scale on the disc.
2. Place the chart on the centre boss of the disc under the plastic lip of the cursor and turn the chart round so that the first period of activity to be measured lines up with the cursor.
3. Hold the chart firm against the disc and slowly move the cursor round to the end of the period of activity being measured (eg driving).
4. Read off the time elapsed from the time scale on the disc.

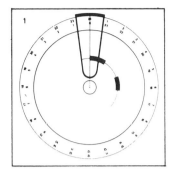

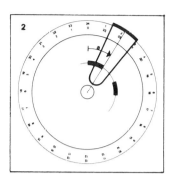

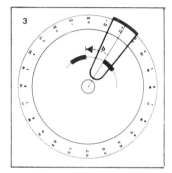

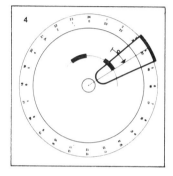

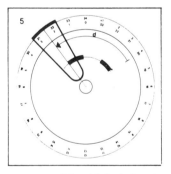

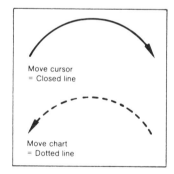

Move cursor
= Closed line

Move chart
= Dotted line

7.1 *Method of evaluation*

Place chart on the analyser and under the cursor, using the appropriate adaptor ring. Set the hairline of the cursor to zero. Then turn the chart until the beginning of the first driving period lines up exactly with the hairline (1). Hold the chart firmly and move cursor to the right over driving period until it lines up with the end of the driving period (2). Then leaving the cursor stationary move chart only to the left until it lines up with the end of the recordings, section b, (3). Again hold the chart firmly and move cursor until its hairline lines up with the end of the second driving period, section c (4). Hold chart firmly and move cursor to the left lining up with the hairline with the first broad recording. The stationary time is now read on the reverse scale under the hairline (5). The same method is applied for all further driving periods. When the hairline has reached the end of the last driving time, the total driving time can be read from the white double scale.

5. Leave the cursor in its new position and revolve the chart further until the same activity commences again.
6. Hold the chart firm and move the cursor again to the end of that further period.
7. Again, read off the time elapsed from the scale on the disc.
8. Repeat this exercise as many times as necessary to measure all the relevant individual activity periods and minimum legal requirements as follows:
   (a) total time from commencing to ending the shift (ie to give total daily working/spreadover time)
   (b) total of break periods (ie to ensure minimum break period requirements are met and, by deducting this time from item (a) above, to give total actual work time);
   (c) cumulative total of driving time (ie to determine maximum daily driving time)
   (d) length of each individual driving period (ie to check maximum continuous driving time in relation to statutory breaks taken).
   See Appendix III for details of current EC drivers' hours law requirements.

These are the times which can be checked with the analysis disc, but certain other items should be checked as follows:

1. Compare the chart against the previous day's chart to ensure that the minimum daily rest period requirement has been observed
2. Check the cumulative daily driving times to ensure that weekly and two-weekly maximum driving limits have not been exceeded.
3. Check that the requisite weekly rest period has been taken and that accumulated rest to compensate for reduced daily and weekly rest periods has also been taken (see Appendix III)

Signing and Retaining the Chart

Once these items have been checked and found to be satisfactory the chart may be signed in a suitable place if desired (this is not legal requirement) and then it must be retained for a least one year, available for inspection if required by an authorised inspecting officer.

Errors on Charts

If charts are found to contain errors and omissions resulting from failure of the driver to complete the centre field correctly; from his failure to indicate his activity modes by correct use of the activity mode switch, because he has exceeded his maximum continuous or total daily driving limits; failed to take the necessary minimum break or rest periods then it is necessary for the employer to take some action.

The precise action to be taken is not specified but EC Regulation 3820/85 (Article 15 {2}) stipulates that, 'if breaches are found to have occurred, the employer shall take appropriate steps to prevent their repetition'. It is obvious that any irregularity should be drawn to the driver's attention with the objective of ensuring that it is not repeated. Since employers have a statutory duty to ensure that records are properly kept and that 'appropriate steps' have been taken following any breach of the rules, and that they may be required to show to a court that they have taken all reasonable steps to do so, the most sensible action would seem to be for a memo to be sent to the driver detailing the error. Such a note should explain what the error or omission was, what he should have done or what the law requires and it should ask him to make sure that it does not happen again. Ideally, the note could ask him to sign to say that he has received the message, that he understands what he has done wrong and agreeing not to repeat the mistake. It is worth also pointing out to him that both he and his employer are liable for prosecution if tachograph records are not properly kept in accordance with the requirements of the law.

A copy of the memo should be kept on file in case a repeat is needed and if a number of similar warnings are necessary the driver should be warned that his actions could lead to his dismissal (subject, of course, to the provisions of employment legislation in this connection).

8: Chart Analysis for Operational Purposes

Fleet operators, both small and large organisations, are anxious to seek ways of effectively recovering their investment in tachographs. Indeed, many grasp the opportunity to collect data about driver and vehicle activities which has not previously been readily available to them. The tachograph manufacturers, and others, give considerable publicity to the possibilities for improved efficiency and greater economy in fleet operations through the use of the instrument and the plethora of chart analysis bureaux (especially in the UK) which have sprung up seems to indicate that there is a market for detailed chart analysis to achieve these objectives.

However, if these particular objectives are to be achieved the fleet operator has to concentrate a great deal of attention on the chart analysis in terms of selecting the system to be used and in its administration. Like any data collection exercise, it is a waste of time if the information collected is not sufficiently accurate to use or if it is not used effectively as the basis on which operating criteria are established and on which management decisions are made.

Basically, three alternatives are open to fleet operators for chart analysis:

1. The use of manual systems in-house.
2. The use of electronic analysis systems, either in-house or through a bureau.
3. The use of computerised systems, either in-house or through a bureau.

The first alternative, the manual system, has both particular advantages and disadvantages. Its prime disadvantage is the slowness of the operation and the physical strain on the person carrying out the work if many charts have to be processed. On the other hand, its particular advantage is that by looking carefully at individual charts more information than the basic operating times of the driver or vehicle will be available. There will be the opportunity to examine recordings in greater detail and, in effect, see the picture behind what is shown on the chart. In other words, all the discrepancies and irregularities in the recordings will be seen as well as the driving manner and the delays.

Similarly, the use of electronic analysis system will provide details of the relevant vehicle/driver operating times from the tachograph chart but without the addition of more than a few items of extra input data. The advantage here is the speed with which a large number of charts can be processed in a busy transport environment and the facility of having the analysed data in printed tabular form for future reference and for comparison purposes, vehicle to vehicle, week to week, and so on.

Computerised systems, whether in-house or through a bureau, will provide summaries and analyses of relevant vehicle/driver operating times as described in Chapter 6 together, in some instances, with other fleet operating data which has been input into the system so the operating information will have been derived from a combination of sources.

With the electronic and computerised analysis systems the emphasis is on measuring time; driving times, working times, break and rest periods of the driver, delivery times and delays and pin-pointing instances of illegal operation where the driver has exceeded his permitted times. With a large volume of charts to process the accuracy of the analyst doing the job comes into question because progressive inaccuracies of a few minutes in the reading process (ie lining up the cursor accurately with the recording) will ultimately distort the end result quite significantly. With the manual system, the emphasis is on accuracy of reading, although this too can suffer at the hands of the analyst, but there is the opportunity to discover important facts from the charts which would inevitably be missed in the massed processing nature of the other systems.

It is important for the fleet operator and manager to determine exactly what information is wanted from tachograph charts and how it is proposed to put that information to use. What also has to be decided is the staff time available for in-house analysis or what budget is available for the use of outside services. So it is a question of priorities of time, cost and benefit/value. There is also to be determined the question of whether the system is to be established for every single chart returned to be methodically examined or whether a detailed analysis is to be carried out periodically on a random selection of charts only.

This chapter is based on the concept of in-house analysis of charts by manual methods in order to calculate operating data and spot the irregularities, determine the quality of the driving methods as well as pin-pointing delays. Where appropriate, the fleet operator can apply the basic principles stated here when using electronic or computerised analysis systems.

Random Checking

The amount of time needed to scan a tachograph chart to see if it reveals any obvious need for further, more detailed, examination is absolutely minimal. Once staff become used to handling and visually scanning charts, they will be able to quickly spot irregularities of recording which require further investigation. Such irregularities, in the main, will concern driving techniques and habits as revealed by the speed trace and journey delays revealed by both the speed and distance traces and the time trace. They will also reveal instances where the tachograph has been opened for illegal or unauthorised purposes and where false or fraudulent marks have been added to the chart.

Regular Monitoring

When chart analysis is carried out on a regular basis, much more systematic monitoring of vehicle performance and utilisation is possible. Such analysis will reveal the driving techniques and delays already mentioned, but it will also enable many other factors to be established.

For example, comparisons can be made of total driving time against total working time, the percentage of delivery/drop time to total driving time, the percentage of loading and delivery time to total working time, the percentage of total working time to paid time (ie when drivers are paid a guaranteed day of so many hours) and various other comparisons.

Such information, gathered regularly across the fleet over a period of time, can be very helpful in determining levels of driver and vehicle utilisation. Furthermore, it reveals useful and positive facts about the time spent loading and making deliveries which, in many operations, is the most time-consuming activity and the one which needs the most careful examination.

What the Charts Reveal

Chart recordings are an important aid to fleet organisation because of the valuable statistical and operational information which they reveal. The results of evaluation give a clear indication of the use to which vehicles are put and the degree of their utilisation. The following list indicates just some of the questions which may be answered as a result of detailed analysis:

1. When was the vehicle used?
2. When did it leave and return to base?
3. How much of the driver's time was spent:
    driving?
    stationary?
    working?
4. How many kilometres were covered?
5. At what average and maximum speed was the vehicle driven?
6. How long were loading and unloading times and how much time was spent waiting at collection and delivery points?
7. How much time was lost by traffic and other delays on the road?
8. What was the overall speed of the vehicle?
9. Was the trip planned rationally?
10. Was the driver's time effectively or fully utilised?
11. How does the performance of this vehicle/driver compare with others in the fleet?

Each recording area on the chart can be examined in detail to provide the answers to such questions.

Working Times
From the moment a driver inserts a chart into the tachograph instrument (assuming the clock is working as it should) recordings begin and continue until it is removed again. So the first piece of information provided is the time of insertion of the chart and time of its removal. This may be important because it can be related to the amount of time the driver spent at work that day (ie his work spread-

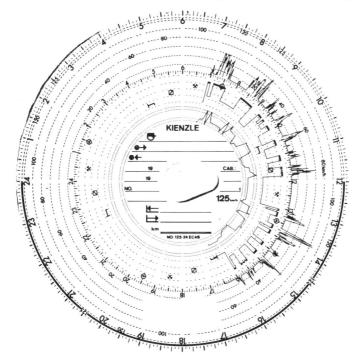

Figure 8.1 *Typical chart showing items mentioned above which can be monitored*

over or shift time). It may reveal that he spent some time working or waiting before or after the chart was in the instrument when any manual entries are examined or if the times are compared to time-clock cards for example.

The time recording on the chart will show – subject to the driver correctly operating the activity mode switch – travel time by means of a broad running line (which will be dealt with later), work periods and break periods.

Work periods should be shown against one or other of the 'work' symbols – passive work or active work. In Europe, EC member states can choose either symbol which may be used to indicate work periods. The passive work symbol indicating attendance at work is mainly used in the UK where there is no specific legal requirement to use the crossed hammers, 'active work', symbol. However, operators may choose to use this for particular purposes, for example loading time or delivery time or time spent at particular locations.

Times shown as other work (active or passive) can be calculated to provide a total for the day. This figure can be compared to total driving time and to total time worked (ie on the clock) thus:

$$\frac{\text{total other work time}}{\text{total driving time}} \times 100 \ = \ \text{X\%}$$

or

$$\frac{\text{total time at work}}{\text{total other work time}} \times 100 \ = \ \text{X\%}$$

This information will show how much of the driver's day was spent in doing work other than driving and how much of his total 'on the clock' time was spent loading, unloading and waiting.

Further examination of the other work time will show how much of this time was incurred before and after the driver's journey or journeys for that day. This may have been time spent in loading and unloading or it may have been time spent waiting for instructions, waiting for delivery notes, waiting while minor repairs were carried out on the vehicle, refuelling and other ancillary activities.

Depending on the amount of such time and the frequency with which it occurs with one driver, a number of drivers or all drivers, a worthwhile piece of information becomes available. Namely, whether there is time wasting by the driver or drivers before and after journeys, or whether drivers are being held up in their work by the inefficiency of traffic office staff or by loading bay staff. And, further, whether excessive time is being spent on minor vehicle repairs or on refuelling which could be done at other times when it does not encroach into the driver's limited legally permissible working day. Queuing for fuel from the operator's own bulk storage supply is an example of significant time loss in many fleets. Additionally, the incidence of regular traffic hold-ups could suggest a need for re-routeing.

Time spent in other work during journeys indicates delivery or collection times or stops for other purposes. In particular, it is important to analyse the time spent on deliveries because delays at certain premises can result in the driver not being able to fulfil his schedule of work for that day or it may mean, because of time limitations, that he has to spend a night away from base which is costly and which disrupts the next day's schedules.

Frequently, drivers complain of delays at particular premises and the tachograph will define precisely the extent of those delays so customers or the people responsible at the premises (which may be the transport firm's own warehouse, depots or shops) can be approached with a view to reducing such delays. With the chart recording showing exact times there can be no argument about the delay, the operator will be able to say, for example, that the vehicle arrived at 11.23am and left at 1.56pm – 2 hours and 33 minutes delay. Such precision in timing will quickly refute comments like 'I saw him arrive and leave and he was only here for about an hour . . . etc'.

In this respect alone, the amount of vehicle operational time which may be saved would be sufficient to more than justify expenditure on staff time in carrying out the analysis.

Break Periods

Examination of break period times is necessary to determine that the statutory minimum legal requirements have been complied with. Since the driver is permitted by the EC regulations to split his breaks into shorter periods (minimum 15 minutes each) and since it is necessary to ensure that sufficient time has been taken in breaks from driving in relation to the continuous driving limit specified by law (see Appendix III), it is important to carefully examine and calculate the time allocated to this item.

Reduction of Stationary Time

Goods vehicles are primarily used for delivery and, therefore, of necessity they spend a proportion of their time in loading and unloading. However, vehicles are earning their keep most effectively when they are moving and the driver's valuable time is being properly utilised for driving. For this reason, the operator needs to look very closely at the time vehicles spend standing, for whatever reasons, and to take active steps to reduce this 'lost' and largely unproductive time as much as possible.

Travelling Time

The chart recording will clearly show the precise times when the vehicle was travelling by means of the broad running trace. Analysis of this activity is easily possible to within a minute so the day's total travel or driving time can be calculated. Total driving time has to be calculated for legal purposes but the figure is also useful for two other specific purposes.

Firstly, when used in conjunction with the total distance travelled it is possible to calculate average driving speed as follows:

$$\frac{\text{Total distance travelled}}{\text{Total driving time}} \times 60 = \text{xkm/hr}$$

This figure can be used for day-to-day or week-by-week comparisons of average driving speed; for comparison between one driver and another; for comparison between a particular regular journey carried out on one day of the week and when it is carried out on another day when traffic congestion is more or less, or when one particular route rather than another is followed.

Average driving speeds used for comparative purposes can provide invaluable basic data for delivery scheduling. It enables the 'best' route to be selected taking account of whichever factor is the most important, time or mileage. It enables the 'best' day to be chosen for covering the route depending on known traffic densities. It enables the driver's day to be most effectively planned to achieve maximum utilisation of driving and delivery time.

Secondly, total time is a factor which can be used for monitoring the utilisation of vehicles and ultimately the economic viability of a fleet of vehicles. The more a vehicle is used the better the return on the capital invested in it. So the operator can make a number of comparisons with this figure as follows:

$$\frac{\text{Total driving time}}{\text{Total duty time}} \times 100 = \text{X\%} \qquad \text{utilisation of shift time}$$

$$\frac{\text{Total driving time}}{24 \text{ hours}} \times 100 = \text{X\%} \qquad \text{utilisation of vehicle availability}$$

Alternatively, with service-type vehicles an indication of time spent 'on the job' can be much more relevant to the operator than actual driving time which may be relatively insignificant. Clearly there is a need to consider these figures along with the other working times because driving time alone when compared to total shift time or total availability time does not present the whole picture. But for the operator contemplating extending his shift working to two or even three daily shifts to obtain greater utilisation of his vehicles, these figures are very informative.

Distance

The distance trace on the chart indicates by each upward and downward stroke every five kilometres covered by the vehicle, so by counting the peaks and multiplying by ten (ie 5km up and 5km down) and then adding in any part-stroke tail ends this will give the distance travelled. Calculation of this figure is helpful as already mentioned for determining average driving speed. It will also confirm the total distance covered as written in on the chart by the driver from his odometer readings at the start and finish of the day.

Furthermore, the operator can calculate the distance covered on any individual journey or on any particular leg of a journey between deliveries. He can see how far the driver travels before his first stop of the day, or how far from base he makes his last stop of the day. Indeed, it is possible in many instances to determine the route the driver took between base and his delivery point by examining the distance recording together with the time recording and relating this to a road map of the area.

Speed Recordings

Driving techniques have a substantial bearing on the cost of operating vehicles and ultimately on the life of vehicle components and the vehicle itself.

The speed recordings on the chart will indicate very clearly the manner of driving and from these recordings the experienced analyst will be able to quickly determine the driver who is costing more money than necessary by his poor style of driving and the one who is economical in his driving.

Principally, the difference is between the erratic driver who see-saws his vehicle along between fierce acceleration and violent braking and the one who follows a smoother course, accelerating progressively and anticipating the need to slow down and stop in plenty of time so that braking is smoother and unhurried. Evidence of these two extremes show clearly on the chart, the former by the wide range of peaks and troughs in the speed trace, the latter by the more compact trace. (See illustration on p 78.)

It is important to recognise the difference between erratic driving and the fluctuations of speed consistent with the movement of dense traffic flows. And, conversely the driver will not produce traces for rural or urban road driving which look like motorway travel. Despite these reservations, however, sufficient evidence will be available to identify the driver who is wearing out the truck's tyres and brakes at an excessive rate, who is causing higher fuel consumption and who is generally knocking 'daylights' out of the engine, transmission and suspension of the vehicle. Also, experience suggests that this is the man who is more likely to run his truck into the back of another with all the costs and aggravation that this means to the operator.

Besides erratic driving the speed trace also confirms a number of other factors. It shows clearly when the vehicle was on motorways and good dual-carriageway roads by means of a fairly constant speed recording. The amount of time spent in

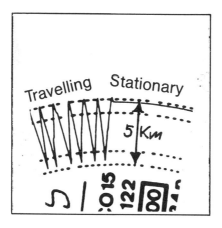

Figure 8.2   *Calculation of distance is by counting the strokes of the distance stylus which total 5km each and 10km for each complete peak*

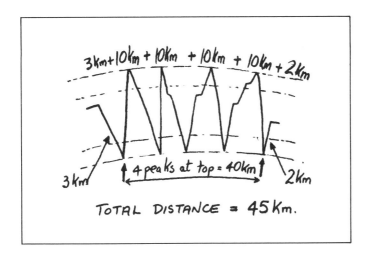

Figure 8.3   *Measuring distance manually*

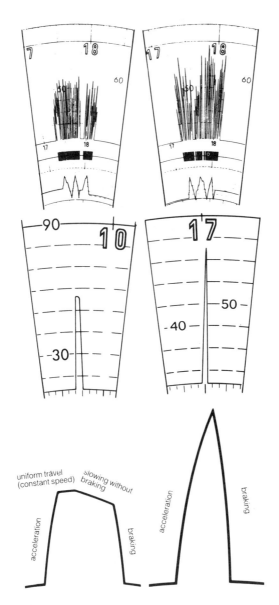

Figure 8.4   *Comparison between typical economical and uneconomical driving*

Typical economic driving	**Typical uneconomic driving**
Rounded peaks not exceeding 60km/h = gradual acceleration to economic speed. Before stopping the vehicle slows down gradually and is only braked briefly.	*Needle-type speed peaks of up to 90km/h indicate sharp acceleration followed immediately by sharp braking.*

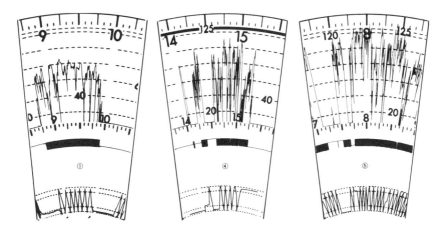

Figure 8.5 *Variations in driving efficiency and their evaluation*

	Assessment scale	**Assessment standard**

The three illustrations above show several driving methods. The diagrams refer to country road traffic where still most of the vehicles are operating.

A comparison of good and uneconomical driving in town traffic is explained in detail on page 76. Here, the prevailing speed restrictions are to be considered.

Characteristic for the operation on motorways and highways are the relatively constant cruising speeds which drop only in case of dense traffic and congestions.

Characteristic recordings of the different types of operation are shown on page 76.

If a scale with 6 marks is applied (individual scales are of course possible) the following marks mentioned in the illustrations would be true.

1 = Exemplary extremely economic driving illustrated by both selection of speed and acceleration and braking.

2 = careful economic driving, road speed within reasonable range, isolated avoidable speed changes and high speeds.

3 = economic driving apart from a few exceptions relating to speed, resp. acceleration and braking.

4 = Fairly economic driving, speeds sometimes too high with erratic acceleration and braking.

5 = insufficiently economic driving, speeds too high, both acceleration and braking too fierce.

6 = driving efficiency in great need of improvement, not economic.

such travel and the distance covered during that time can be calculated (see illustration p 77). It also shows when vehicles are held up in traffic jams and have to crawl along at about walking pace. The speed trace will show this, and both the time and distance recordings will confirm when and for how long the situation lasted and over what distance.

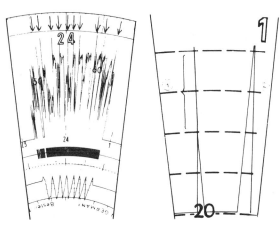

Figure 8.6   Speed peaks caused by rear axle gear change
In the case of vehicles with a two speed rear axle, fine peaks which clearly exceed the normal road speed, occur in the recording when the rear axle gear change is operated. These peaks bear no relationship to true road speed. Frequency and the exact time of gear change operation can easily be recognised. The right-hand illustration shows in principle the difference between 'driven peak' and 'gear-change peak'.

1 = gear-change peak, fine needle peak, reason: instantaneous rise and fall of road speed stylus.

2 = driven peak, it 'stands on two legs', because time has elapsed during upward and downward movement of the stylus.

Time

All these activities of speed and distance, work and breaks can be related to precise periods of time on the time scale of the chart so each activity can be judged accurately to within one minute with the aid of an optical chart analyser (see p 55).

Analysing the Chart

Analysis of charts for the purposes described is easily accomplished by clerical staff with a small amount of training and with the optical analyser. The process of making the analysis is as described in Chapter 7. The chart is placed on the chart disc and revolved against the cursor with each particular activity to be examined being measured separately.

The data obtained may be recorded in a format to suit the operator depending on the type of work and the data which will be most useful for planning and decision-making purposes. This data may be recorded on a simple form drawn up to suit the purpose and containing the following headings:

1. Total duty time
2. Total driving time
3. Total distance travelled
4. Length of driving periods
5. Distance covered in driving periods
6. Average speed for day
7. Average speed for driving periods
8. Number of breaks
9. Total time for breaks
10. Number of deliveries
11. Total time for deliveries
12. Average time per delivery
13. Time loss before starting driving
14. Time loss after finishing driving
15. Time between deliveries
16. Distance between deliveries
17. Distance covered on rural/urban roads
18. Distance covered on dual-carriageway/motorway roads
19. Time at work before . . . am
20. Time at work after . . . pm
21. Percentage actual work time to maximum 'on-clock' time
22. Percentage actual driving time to maximum driving time
23. Percentage driving time to actual work time
24. Percentage driving time to total vehicle availability time
25. Assessment of unnecessary delay time
26. Assessment of unnecessary distance covered
27. Number of times exceeded . . . km/hr
28. Assessment of driving technique
    Very good
    Good/Normal
    Poor

It is easy to devise further headings in addition to those shown here to suit particular purposes or to delete any not required.

Alternatively, with computerised systems a driver/vehicle database can be established on a once-and-for-all basis, enabling data to be logged and later called up to reveal relevant information such as the performance of individual drivers and particular vehicles in isolation or for comparative purposes.

Irregularities on Charts

The majority of heavy goods vehicle drivers will find no good reason or need to produce anything other than perfectly good and legal chart recordings. On the other hand there will always be a few who for various reasons will attempt to alter, interfere with, or inhibit recordings in some way or other. The examination of charts under an optical analyser will quickly reveal irregularities to the experienced observer. Before examining these activities in detail it is important to point out that such actions are totally illegal and could result in the driver facing serious charges with the prospect of heavy financial penalties, plus the risk of loss of his HGV driving licence and, in extreme cases the possibility of a prison sentence.

Generally, interference with recordings will follow a number of common patterns as follows:

1. Speed stylus inhibited or bent
2. Instrument opened and clock wound back
3. Hand-made recordings
4. Clock jammed or stopped.

Inhibited or Bent Speed Stylus

If the driver wishes to disguise his actual travel speed he may resort to one or other of two alternative actions. He may wedge an obstruction in the speed stylus slot in the back of the instrument to prevent the stylus riding as high on the chart scale as the vehicle actually travelled – thus showing a lower maximum speed. This, however, will cause the speed recording to appear on the chart with a 'flat' top and calculation of the average speed over the relevant period will indicate that such action has been taken.

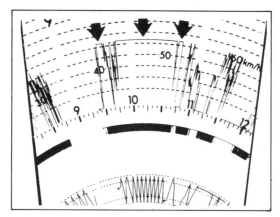

Figure 8.7   *Speed recording shows lower maximum speed than travelled by the vehicle*

$$\left(ie \quad \frac{distance}{time} \; = \; average \; speed \right)$$

A variation on this is when the obstruction is spongy in nature thereby not totally preventing the stylus from moving at the top of its permitted range but still inhibiting it in making a proper recording. The trace made in such circumstances is particularly characteristic and noticeable. If the speed stylus is bent downwards to disguise the top speed achieved, the stylus will record below the base line when the vehicle returns to rest.

Instrument Opened and Clock Turned Back

This practice will be indulged in by drivers who divert off route for their own purposes and then wish to disguise the time loss. However, when the clock is turned back it is likely that either a gap or an overlapped recording will appear on all three traces, (ie speed, time and distance) and more particularly, the distance trace will not link up properly because the stylus will have continued to operate on its up and down path while the vehicle is travelling even though the instrument face is open. A further point to note is that the odometer continues to record distance travelled while the face is open, so the total daily recorded distance on the odometer will be in excess of the distance recorded on the chart (ie by the amount of running by the vehicle when the instrument face was open).

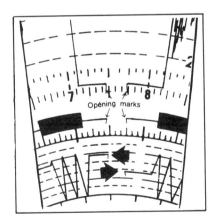

Figure 8.8   *Opening of the instrument face and moving the vehicle will result in a gap in the recording and the distance stylus recording not lining up*

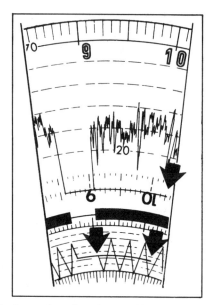

Figure 8.9   *Opening the face and moving, then winding the clock back will produce this type of recording*

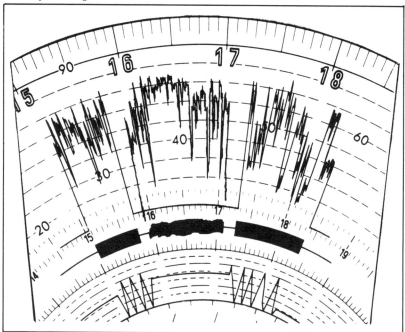

Figure 8.10   *Manually entered recordings are easily distinguishable by their irregularity and unnatural appearance. Frequently the 'artist' allows lines to lean backwards which would not be possible with proper recordings and there is usually no proper calculation of the ratio of speed to distance so vast discrepancies in average speed arise.*

Hand-Made Recordings

Attempts by the driver to 'fill in' or manually create false recordings on charts for a variety of reasons are invariably detectable instantly by a skilled (or even not so skilled) chart analyst. It is impossible in practical terms for the driver to be able to produce a full and correct recording by this means (although the author has seen some convincing attempts) since his skill with the sharp object used to make the false recording needs to be more than matched by his skill as a mathematician because he must ensure that the time and distance functions equate to the speed trace otherwise an average speed which is too high or too low compared to the actual speed shown will result (see Chapter 13 for example).

Clock Stopping

Stopping the clock, either by jamming the works or disconnecting the electric power supply, will, of course, prevent the chart from rotating in the instrument and thus if the vehicle is driven in this condition with the instrument face closed then both the speed and distance styli will continue to record but on the same path so that a single thick black line trace will appear in each recording area. If this is permitted to persist for too long there is a danger of the styli puncturing the chart and then tearing it which completely invalidates its use as a legal record and in the process damaging the styli to an extent which would involve repair or complete replacement at an approved workshop.

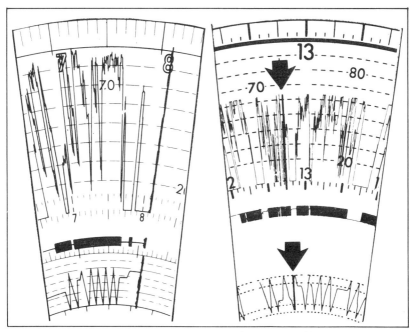

Figure 8.11 *Two examples of clock stopping (a) a complete stoppage (b) a temporary stop then correct function afterwards.*

It should be added that a clock stoppage through malfunction rather than driver interference has the same effect and for this reason the driver should be vigilant in observing the clock indicator in the face of the instrument.

Other Irregularities

A wide range of further irregularities may come to light if tachograph systems are carefully monitored. For example, the author has come across instances where charts have been removed with the vehicle on the move and the next day's chart replaced while still on the move. This particular 'dodge' was used in an attempt to cover up the fact that drivers were returning home at night rather than take a night out which, to conform to the law, they should have done. The give away was the way in which the speed trace on the chart faded out at some 30/40kph instead of returning to the base line which it would always do when the vehicles comes to rest. Similarly the next day's chart started with a speed recording in the 30/40kph area rather than from the speed base line.

Manipulation of charts and use of more than one chart on a day is, of course, illegal but it is a practice which may occur unless management is vigilant in its checking of charts. Lack of a specific legal requirement to number charts individually and have drivers account for them as before (and as with the old written records) has opened up the possibility for this practice to operate.

9: Accident Evaluation from Charts

Among the many roles fulfilled by the data which can be determined from a tachograph chart, providing factual evidence of the circumstances of a motor vehicle accident can be the most critical; and to the parties involved, crucial in establishing their responsibility or otherwise for causing the accident and their guilt or otherwise if charges are laid by the police for motoring offences following the accident.

The events which occur in the period immediately prior to and at the precise moment of an accident are often surrounded in mystery. The driver perhaps cannot remember precisely, or is unsure of his speed and sometimes, even, his actions. Drivers of other vehicles involved have similar problems and when witnesses and bystanders report their impressions these are not always consistent with them having actually 'seen' the accident. Often, their statements are based on assumptions having seen the aftermath of the accident and invariably their impression of the vehicle speed prior to the accident is widely exaggerated.

Human Estimates

Extensive tests carried out in West Germany have shown conclusively the inability of man to correctly and accurately assess factors of speed or distance. Specific tests show that participants' error varied between 146 per cent and 228 per cent on distance estimates and between 57 per cent and 130 per cent on speed estimates of passing vehicles. Certain vehicles involved in the series of experiments were particularly noisy, and passed with the horn blowing and lights flashing. In these cases the percentage of error was exceptionally high.

Clearly these tests confirm the unreliability of accident witnesses' ability to accurately report and recount matters relating to the events immediately before an accident and at the moment of impact. Consequently, if the driver's recollection of the situation is blurred and witness reports are not dependable in many instances there can be no real judgement on the cause of an accident or where the blame lies. Unfortunately, in many such instances blame automatically rests with the driver and he may find it extremely difficult to convince his employer, the insurers and the police of the true facts of the case.

Tachograph Accuracy

It is in these circumstances that the ability of the tachograph to record, very accurately, details of speed and distance – in fact, to within a minute or even less and to within a metre – against a time scale can prove the instrument's true value to drivers and vehicle owners alike. Extensive use has been made of tachograph charts in accident analysis for many years and in the UK there is increasing use of chart analysis for this purpose. The events surrounding a number of fatal vehicle accidents in recent years have been determined in this manner, to the considerable benefit of the driver in some of these cases when he may have otherwise had very little evidence on his side and when witness reports may have been unfavourable or even hostile towards him.

Microscopic analysis of tachograph charts following accidents requires very specialised knowledge and equipment and for the information to be acceptable in court it is important for the analysis to be seen to have been independently and expertly carried out. The major tachograph manufacturers have facilities or can make arrangements for carrying out such analysis and so too have certain independent specialists. The Metropolitan Police Forensic Laboratory and other regional Police Forensic Laboratories (five in the UK) have an accident analysis capability. Kienzle of West Germany and Lucas Kienzle in the UK have extensive experience in this work and for many years have provided independent evidence to the courts in respect of accident inquests and investigations. This follows a procedure patented by Kienzle in 1953.

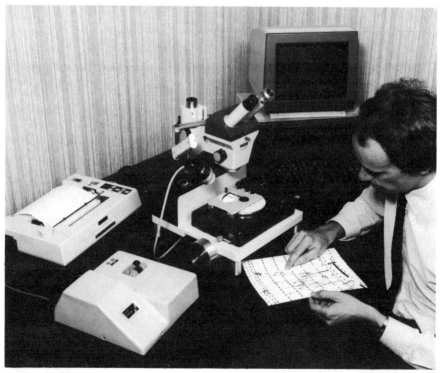

Figure 9.1   *Accident evaluation from a tachograph chart using a computer-based electro-binocular microscope.*

The relevant section of the chart containing the record of the vehicle impact is isolated and magnified from 16 up to 60 times to reveal the pattern of movement leading up to the impact and details of the impact itself. What the magnification shows is the precise speed at which the vehicle was travelling at the moment of impact. Working back from this, using a cursor which is a beam of light only 3 microns (ie 3/1000mm) thick, the speed trace shows the speed from which the vehicle had slowed to the point of impact (unless the impact occurred during acceleration) and the speed pattern prior to slowing before the impact.

Measured against the time scale of the chart and the distance recording, an expert analyser can determine the precise rates of acceleration and deceleration of the vehicle in metres per second per second (ie m/sec^2) or 'g'. Using this technique, a diagrammatic extrapolation of speed against time and distance can be made and from this the actual vehicle activity can be recounted. For example, it could be stated that in a particular instance (see Figure 9.2) a vehicle was accelerating from 40km/hr at 850 metres before an impact to 65km/hr at 200 metres before the impact covering this 650 metres in 44 seconds. It then slowed to 60km/hr in a period of 11 seconds and over a distance of 180 metres then decelerated violently in a period of one second to 51km/hr at which point the impact occurred.

In the analysis process, the time between marked speed changes is measured with the aid of the cursor which is set perpendicular to the path of the recording stylus. The beam of light which comprises the cursor is reflected vertically from the deepest point of the engraved trace and becomes visible in the microscope.

The Facts

This information is most valuable in relation to the activity of this vehicle but if the collision was with another vehicle, which also had a tachograph, then microscopic analysis of both charts would reveal very significant facts about the whole incident.

It is important to note the use of the word *facts* because this is what the chart analysis provides, independent and unbiased facts. Unlike the statements of witnesses the chart does not give impressions, opinions, assumptions or conjecture about the incident. It is not influenced by the noise of the passing vehicle, the squeal of tyres or the horrific sounds of the crash all of which colour witness reactions and comments. When the information is presented to the court a 10x photographic enlargement of the accident section of the chart is provided in addition to the speed/time/distance graph.

Accident Evaluation Case Studies

Reproduced by special permission of Lucas Kienzle Instruments Limited
These German case studies are taken from the files of Mannesmann Kienzle GmbH which has conducted tens of thousands of such evaluations. They are representative of a wide range of vehicle accidents and vehicle-related incidents and they illustrate the manner in which microscopic evaluations are carried out and the facts prepared for presentation to the court.

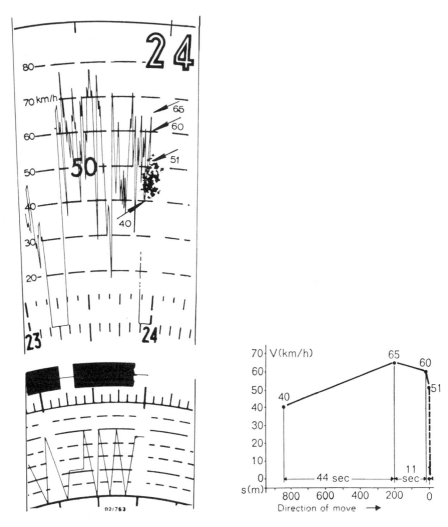

Figure 9.2 *Section of chart and analysis diagrams to illustrate the example on page 89*

Case No 1

Tachograph chart contributes to an acquittal

The accused driver was charged with having driven his lorry on to the motorway without observing an articulated truck travelling from the left, already on the motorway. This truck ran into the lorry and the driver received injuries.

According to the accused's statement, the articulated truck was not visible at the point where he joined the motorway. This did not conflict with the expert opinion of Kienzle, according to which a driver coming on to the motorway would have 400 to 500 metres visibility to the rear. According to the information read from the tachograph charts of both vehicles, the articulated truck could have been a maximum of 510 metres and a minimum of 340 metres away. The incoming lorry accelerated from 0 to 24km/h. The speed of the articulated truck, on the other hand, was between 66 and 70km/h until shortly before the impact and it was particularly noted that the driver did not brake to any appreciable extent. As his stopping distance would have been only 80 metres a collision was unavoidable.

Therefore, it was clearly a case of a collision accident in which no blame could be attached to the accused. Result: Acquittal of the accused driver.

Case No 2

Safe-breakers caught with the aid of the chart

It reads like a TV crime story. The theft of a safe from the head office of a farmers' co-operative was reported to the police. The initial investigation showed that the safe, a welding set and the organisation's own transporter were missing. The next morning the vehicle with the safe cut open was found 40km away from the scene of the crime; the chart was still in the tachograph.

Visual interpretation produced the following information: At 00.23 hours the thieves drove away from the scene of the crime travelled some 65km parked the vehicle for 38 minutes and then drove a further 16.3km. If it was assumed that the 38-minute stop was actual 'working time' (cutting the safe open), the place concerned had to be 16.3km from the point where the vehicle was found.

First of all, the chart came to the Kienzle analysis department for the driving and stopping times to be precisely determined. These figures were then converted into distances so that the probable route taken by the vehicle could be reconstructed. The police took a series of night drives as near to the same time of night as the thieves committed the offence. After several vain attempts a junk-yard was found, which was some way away from the nearest village. Enquiries at the local police office revealed that the owner of the scrap business was a prisoner who was on the run at the time. There was a good chance that the safe had been cut open in this junk-yard.

When a search was carried out shortly afterwards at the homes of employees of the scrap firm – in connection with another burglary – among other articles were found items from the burglary at the co-operative. The chain of evidence was complete and the culprits were convicted.

Case No 3

Evaluation under the microscope revealed discrepancies

It happened shortly after midnight. On the motorway a heavy truck and trailer ran into a lorry in front of it, at a fairly high speed. There was extensive damage and the driver's mate in the truck and trailer suffered fatal injuries.

The charts from the tachograph on both vehicles were passed by the police to a motor vehicle expert for interpretation and he came to the following conclusion:

1. The truck with trailer had run into the lorry at about 67 km/h, since its chart showed violent deflections around this speed which pointed to an impact.

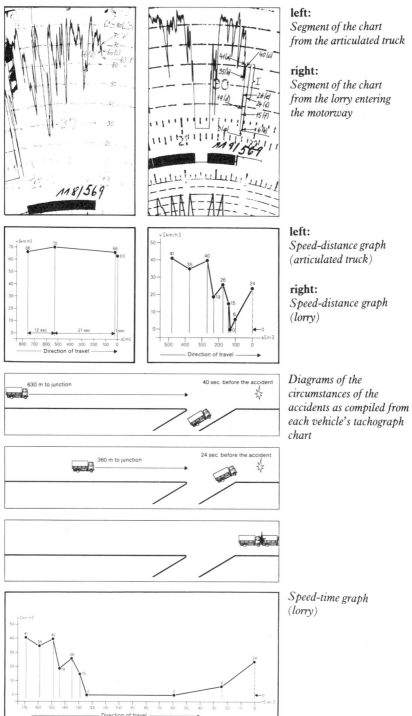

left:
Segment of the chart from the articulated truck

right:
Segment of the chart from the lorry entering the motorway

left:
Speed-distance graph (articulated truck)

right:
Speed-distance graph (lorry)

Diagrams of the circumstances of the accidents as compiled from each vehicle's tachograph chart

Speed-time graph (lorry)

Figure 9.3   *Section of chart and analysis diagrams for accident evaluation case no 1*

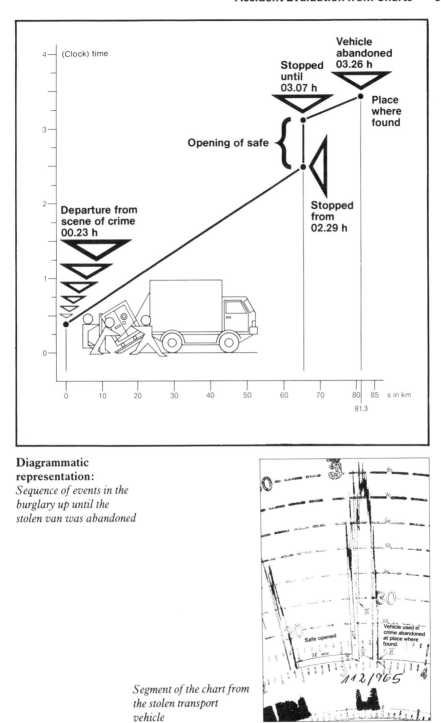

Diagrammatic representation:
Sequence of events in the burglary up until the stolen van was abandoned

Segment of the chart from the stolen transport vehicle

Figure 9.4   *Section of chart and analysis diagrams for accident evaluation case no 2*

2. The lorry in front had been travelling at a speed of 40-50km/h and had then slowed down to some 30km/h. A 'centrifugal peak' – an abrupt upward deflection on the speed recording stylus – pointed to actuation of the gear shift, after which the lorry clearly came to a standstill; after being stationary for a period of 15 minutes there was a deflection of the time recording stylus which the expert construed as an impact. Consequently, the cause of the accident was found to be due to the lorry stopping on the motorway contrary to regulations

Analysis under the microscope at Kienzle, on the other hand, produced a different picture. The truck and trailer did indeed crash into the lorry at 67km/h but the analysis of events before the collision was wrong. In contrast with it the 'evaluation' of the chart from the rammed lorry showed up two crucial errors:

Error No 1
The anomalous recording interpreted by the expert as a centrifugal peak marked the moment of impact, when the speed recording stylus was thrown upwards a long way.

Error No 2
The relatively small deflection of the time recorder stylus some 15 minutes after the vehicle came to a standstill was too insignificant to be regarded an an indication of impact. The vibrations that occurred would have appeared as more pronounced stylus deflections.

The Kienzle analysis proved that the lorry in front was travelling at a speed of some 30km/h at the moment of impact. The idea that the accident had been caused by the first lorry stopping on the motorway contrary to regulations could clearly be refuted.

Case No 4

Even here an analysis was possible
At night on the motorway, a truck with trailer was obliged to stop because of a fractured oil pipe. A few minutes later a second truck and trailer ran into the stationary vehicle at a speed which was at first unknown. There was extensive material damage; the driver and mate of the truck that crashed into it were seriously injured.

How could this accident happen? No blame was attached to the driver of the stationary truck and trailer; a trail of oil a kilometre long was obvious proof of the defect and the necessary stop. Evidently there was human failure of the following driver who did not notice the warning signals given with a torch and hence braked too late. Other circumstances could be excluded. The road was dry and the prevailing weather conditions were good. There was no question of mechanical failure on this vehicle.

The reasoning for this deduction was made difficult by the fact that the tachograph of the crashing truck was totally destroyed and the chart was badly damaged. However, the Kienzle accident evaluation department attempted the

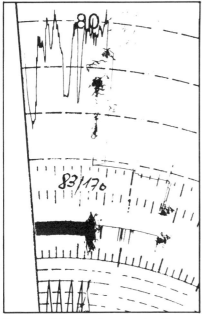

Segment of the chart (truck and trailer coming up behind)

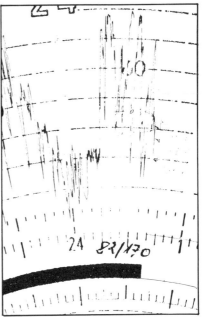

Segment of the chart (lorry in front)

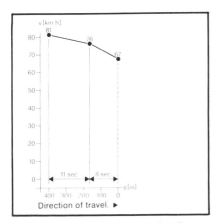

Speed-distance graph (truck and trailer coming up behind)

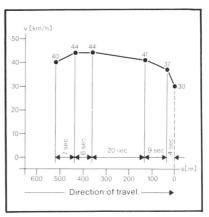

Speed-distance graph (lorry in front)

Figure 9.5 *Sections of chart and analysis diagrams for accident evaluation case no 3*

almost impossible – but eventually succeeded. After scrupulous microscopic investigations, they succeeded in revealing the precise speed graph which led to the following result: Before reaching the place where the accident took place, the driver of the truck coming up behind had increased the speed of this vehicle over a distance of 405 metres from 60 to 67km/h. At 20 metres before the impact he braked, but could only bring the speed down to 64km/h.

Thus, evidence was presented of carelessness with serious consequences, circumstances that maybe would have never been made known.

Case No 5

Chart leads to court proceedings being dropped

On the motorway near Limburg (West Germany), because of slippery snow, a long distance truck with trailer got into a skid in a brief braking operation and veered out on to the overtaking lane. The driver of the following estate car did not have time to stop, ran into the truck and was wedged between the towing vehicle and the trailer. There was considerable damage. According to the police report, the truck was being driven at too high a speed considering the road and weather conditions at the time of the accident. The tracks on the road seemed to confirm this. The public prosecutor's office instituted proceedings against the truck driver and he came up for trial.

At the start of the trial the defence applied for a microscopic analysis of the chart recovered from the truck. This analysis, carried out by Kienzle, had the following outcome: The truck driver reduced the speed of his truck and trailer from an initial 77km/h to about 30km/h by degrees, accelerated over a distance of 80 metres to some 34km/h and maintained this speed for about 65 metres. Then he slowed down again gently over a distance of 55 metres to some 31km/h. Only then did the driver brake, the wheels briefly locked and the vehicle started to jack-knife at 13km/h. It speaks for the skill of the driver that in this critical situation he accelerated from his speed of 13km/h to 24km/h to straighten his vehicle out again, before he finally applied the brakes.

This interpretation convinced the court and the case was dropped. In the reasons given, it was stated that the driver had acted correctly in the conditions caused by the weather. The analysis of the chart had clearly shown this.

Developments in Accident Evaluation

Considerable developments in the techniques for accident evaluation from tacograph charts have taken place in recent times. Lucas Kienzle in the UK has become expert in its own right and a leader in this field. The company has established computerised facilities which improve the efficiency, accuracy and speed of the analysis process. In due course case studies based on UK accidents will become available for publication.

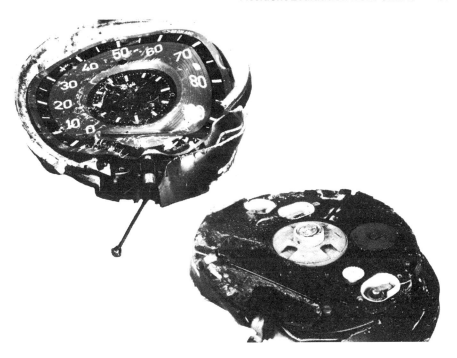

The parts of the shattered tachograph with the damaged chart

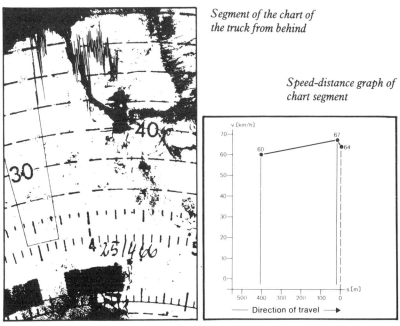

Segment of the chart of the truck from behind

Speed-distance graph of chart segment

Figure 9.6   *The tacograph, section of chart and analysis diagram for accident evaluation case no 4*

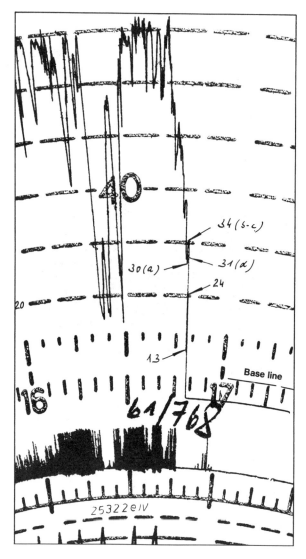

*Segment of the chart of
the long-distance truck
and trailer*

*Speed-distance graph
with details of times*

Figure 9.7 *Section of chart and analysis
diagram for accident evaluation case no 5*

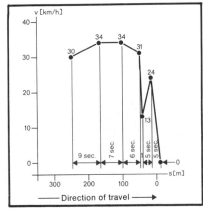

10: The Driver, Tachographs and Productivity

The introduction of tachographs into the working life of most heavy goods vehicle drivers had a significant impact on their attitudes and their activities. In the main, if the driver does a good and honest day's work the tachograph will prove to be useful to him. It saves him laboriously writing out daily record sheets and weekly reports. The recordings show that he has done his work properly and that he has complied with the law. They also confirm what he says about delays on the road and about delays at delivery points, customer premises and even in his own depot, and they confirm that he is driving his vehicle safely and economically.

In other words, the evidence on the chart will confirm to the employer the professionalism of the driver. Conversely, it will clearly expose the antics of the not so professional driver: the man who is always seeking to 'cut corners', do half a job and claim the maximum benefit for it, and who turns every operation around to suit his own ends. While there are but few of these drivers about, those who do exist will see how the tachograph inhibits their activities. These people, of course, are the ones who complain loudest and longest about the unfairness of tachographs, about 'spy in the cab' management and the iniquity of the 'system'.

Speeding

Most drivers' fear of tachographs is related to the vexed question of evidence of speeding. There are two aspects of this problem to be considered – one concerns the employer, the other the legal situation.

Firstly, as far as the employer is concerned, he may, as company policy, set maximum speed limits for his vehicles which are below the legally permitted maximum speed for the vehicle (ie currently 60mph for heavy vehicles on motorways, 50mph on dual-carriageways and 40mph on other non-restricted roads). Drivers can be made aware of these set limits by the speed warning light on the instrument which illuminates when the set speed is exceeded. Clearly, the employer, in setting such limits, would have sound reasons for doing so which the driver would be aware of and for which some process of disciplinary action for breaches of the limit would be laid down in company rules. In these circumstances the driver knows what to expect if he breaks the rules.

Secondly, there is the question of tachograph evidence when a driver has been speeding. The situation here is quite clear, as follows:

1. If the driver is apprehended by the police for speeding on the evidence of their normal methods (ie by pacing with a patrol car, by radar, vascar or other

speed-measuring device) then he will be warned that prosecution may follow.

If the police, at the time of stopping the driver, ask to see his tachograph chart – which they are entitled to do – and this confirms their evidence of speed then they *may* call for the chart to be produced as prosecution evidence. If, on the other hand, the chart shows a speed difference to that which he has been accused of then the drive *could* produce that chart in court in his defence. If he is to do this it would be wise to request the police officer to sign his chart at the time he is stopped so there is no question of him producing in court a chart which is disputed as not being the relevant one. Then it is necessary to have the chart properly analysed so that the recording of speed which is in kph can be accurately converted in mph which is the basis for the prosecution.

When he produces his chart, it is up to the court to decide whether to accept it as evidence and, if it does, whether it is sufficient proof that the police case is not sound and, therefore the case should be dismissed, most likely on the grounds that the evidence of the chart casts doubt on the police evidence. In order for this to happen, however, it is likely that a significant difference in speed would need to be shown to convince the court.

2. If the driver is stopped by the police during the day for a particular reason (eg in a roadside check) and he is asked to produce his tachograph chart, then if the chart shows that earlier in the day (or on a previous day's chart if this is requested) he had been driving at more than 60mph (ie over the maximum limit on any road) the police will not prosecute for speeding solely on this retrospective evidence. They may prosecute for reckless driving if the speed was excessive and there was other evidence to back this up – an accident for example. In order to bring about a prosecution for speeding, evidence must be produced showing:

   (a) The speed at which the vehicle was travelling (which the chart confirms);
   (b) The time at which the vehicle was travelling at the alleged speed (which the chart also confirms);
   (c) The precise location (ie the section of road) where the vehicle was travelling at the alleged speed (which the chart *does not* show).

It is because of this missing piece of vital evidence that drivers will not be prosecuted for speeding on the basis of tachograph chart recordings alone.

A useful point to note from the employer's point of view in regard to traces showing driving in excess of 60mph, is that if enforcement staffs notice this when carrying out routine checks of the charts they may note the fact for future reference. If the employer finds that his drivers are regularly exceeding speed limits, it would be prudent to request drivers to keep their driving within the legal limits.

There have been a number of cases in the UK where hgv drivers have been suspended from driving for periods of time by the Licensing Authorities as a penalty for persistent speeding as shown by their tachograph charts. The authorities are also considering the imposition of regulations requiring compulsory fitment of road speed limiters on goods vehicles (as with the legal requirement for coaches).

Evidence of a general trend by employers in the industry to voluntarily curtail vehicle speeds might go some way towards reducing the likelihood of this step being taken.

Production of Charts

A driver may be asked to produce for examination the chart in his tachograph and the charts for preceding days in that week and the last day of the previous driving week (see p 138). By law, he must permit an authorised examiner or police officer to examine charts and to remove or take away the charts for examination if necessary.

When the charts are examined, the driver should ask the examiner or police officer to sign the chart as evidence of its inspection. If the charts are to be taken away (impounded) the driver must obtain a receipt showing the date and time, the name and address of the person taking them, and the dates of the charts which have been taken. Usually a receipt signature will be given on the reverse of the next blank chart which is to be used to replace those confiscated. This is a safeguard in the event that the driver is asked to produce charts which he no longer has in his possession, to prove to his employer that the charts have been taken and to enable his employer to account for missing charts if an examiner visits his premises before the particular charts are returned.

Driving Techniques

The manner in which a vehicle is driven can have a significant effect on its fuel consumption and the overall cost of its operation. Since the tachograph chart clearly reveals evidence of differing driving techniques between good and poor, the driver will want to take steps to improve his driving methods. Many operators correctly using tachographs have found that drivers are well aware of what the charts reveal and that they regularly compare charts to see who is the 'best' driver. Such voluntary comparison and competition provides beneficial results for the operator by way of reduced fuel consumption and reduced wear and tear costs on his vehicles (particularly tyres and brake linings).

The following points may be helpful to improve driving techniques:

1. Drive in such a way that a steady speed can be maintained over a fairly long stretch of road.
2. Keep to an economic speed. This is generally two-thirds of the maximum speed but is it may differ depending on the road, traffic and weather conditions and the vehicle.
3. Avoid unnecessary speed peaks except when overtaking. These bursts of speed do not save time.
4. Anticipate road conditions ahead and drive steadily. The real art of good driving is recognising difficult traffic conditions in plenty of time and planning necessary changes in speed or direction well in advance.
5. Use the vehicle brakes as little as possible. Braking involves a loss of 'energy'. Easing back on the accelerator pedal earlier often has the same braking effect.

6. Drive with the accelerator pedal held steadily. When the desired cruising speed is achieved, allow the pedal to come up until the speed is maintained with a minimum throttle opening. Driving with the pedal down an extra inch provides little extra speed but it does use extra fuel.

Driving smoothly and progressively within the law usually allows the same distance to be covered in a specific period of time as that covered by the speeding driver but with greater comfort and safety, with less cost and no risk of prosecution for speeding or bad driving.

Driver Productivity

Information gained from tachograph chart analysis can materially assist management in assessing vehicle productivity and in taking decisive steps to improve such productivity. The driver will have a specific interest and involvement in this because his actions can have an effect on the degree of productivity achieved. He can be instrumental in improving average operating speeds, in reducing delays to vehicles at base, in reducing delays on the road by choosing 'better' routes, in reducing delays at delivery points by accurately reporting the reasons where these are obvious, and in driving the vehicle more economically.

Because of the vital role of drivers in this matter there are grounds for looking at ways in which they can be directly rewarded in relation to improvements against measured standards. Often bonus schemes cannot be established because basic data for monitoring and bonus assessment is not readily available. The tachograph readily provides a variety of information which can be adopted for use in bonus schemes.

A great deal has been talked about the ways in which the tachograph may be used to establish productivity schemes for payment for drivers and to establish incentives which will encourage greater vehicle productivity and efficiency of operation. However, as yet, it appears too early to be able to relate particular experiences of fleet operators in this respect because while many have the objective in mind very few indeed have found a successful formula for putting such schemes into practice. In the main, driver payment systems remain related to hours worked (basic time plus overtime) or to some formula of productivity based on the number of deliveries made and completion of tasks within predetermined times.

One of the significant aspects of the introduction of tachographs is the immediate effect which their use has on existing average-speed related productivity schemes. In most cases such schemes are calculated on travel speeds varying commonly between a low of 21mph and a high of 27mph. While the driver used a written log book he could effectively fill his day, arriving back at base at the expected time having achieved the average speed and completed his deliveries. What the record did not show was his speed of travel between stops, and how many stops he actually had during the day. With the tachograph in use the driver will either have to continue to travel as before and show all his stops (and invariably there will be a number because most schemes have plenty of slack time in them) or he will have to endeavour to keep his vehicle speed down to levels which will equate with the average speed of the productivity scheme. He will find this difficult; it will be boring in the extreme and likely to cause a hazard travelling so slowly on motorways.

Thus before firms can get down to planning tachograph-based productivity schemes, they will have to reappraise any pre-existing schemes and persuade drivers to overcome their natural reluctance (except where the payment system encourages them otherwise) to bring vehicles back into the depot before the end of the allotted time for the journey. Similarly, drivers who are on guaranteed paid-hours payment schemes will be reluctant to show the job can be done in less time by arriving back at the depot early. These are major obstacles which management has to overcome before it can look ahead to new schemes.

Assuming that these problems can be overcome then new discussions on payment schemes can take place based on factors which can be determined from tachograph chart recordings. A whole list of potential bases for chart-derived payment schemes can be suggested but it is worth pointing out that they are dependent upon a number of critical conditions being fulfilled:

1. Recordings must be accurate.
2. Proper and accurate analysis of recordings must take place.
3. Drivers will have to accept the accuracy of the analysis if they are to agree to the scheme in principle and its day-to-day operation.

From the fleet operator's point of view, any scheme should be related to factors which achieve certain objectives as follows:

1. Improved load factor utilisation of vehicles.
2. Minimum route mileages.
3. Reduced delays and downtime.
4. Reduced vehicle operating costs especially in regard to fuel, tyres and repair costs.

Driver's wages constitute one of the largest single cost items in vehicle operations but to suggest reductions in wages costs is verging on sacrilege. Few drivers will accept real reductions in pay even for less work and it is a courageous management who would suggest such an approach. However, there is the prospect that by better scheduling resulting from improved vehicle productivity, it may be possible for an operator to fulfil his obligations with fewer vehicles, and if he can do this then real and substantial savings will be made both by the saving of the vehicle standing and running costs and by the saving of the driver costs.

Assuming that the difficulties referred to earlier can be overcome, the way is open to consider how some of the following factors may be applied to a productivity payment scheme:

1. *Improved average travel speed* – eg a 5mph increase in average speed from 25mph to 30mph on a 200 mile journey saves almost $1\frac{1}{2}$ hours running time.
2. *Reduced drop times* – while these are often outside the control of the driver they are not exclusively so and many firms using tachographs have used chart evidence to put pressure on delivery points for more rapid vehicle turn-round with considerable success.

3. *Reduced time losses at base* – this is an area where considerable time wastage occurs, often created by people who have no appreciation of the pressure on the driver's working day or indeed of the costs of keeping a vehicle standing waiting. Elimination of this wastage can substantially improve driver productivity and reduce the level of payment to him for standing idle while other people in the organisation get themselves sorted out.

4. *Reduced route mileage on regular journeys* – reducing route mileage saves costs related to vehicle running – fuel, tyres etc – and saves driver time, thus more effective route planning to keep mileages to a minimum will be beneficial in getting the driver back to base sooner with the possibility of reusing or reloading the vehicle or reducing driver overtime.

5. *Improved utilisation of maximum driving time* – it is essential to secure maximum utilisation of the driver's limited driving time (normally 9 hours daily) especially on long distance and trunking-type operations. This is only effectively achieved if acceptable speeds are maintained for the journey on the one hand and maximum use is made of the vehicle load capacity on the other hand. High average speeds with half-empty trucks are not examples of high utilisation – one aspect negates the other.

6. *Improved driving time to working time relationship* – depending on the nature of the operation it can be important for the driver to spend as much of his working time as possible actually behind the wheel driving. Most drivers are paid premium wage rates to drive so it is essential that diversionary activities are reduced to a minimum to allow them to achieve a full legal shift of driving. Too often valuable driving time is taken up with other non-essential, even useless, tasks better delegated to other staff who are not constrained by legal limits on their working times. A low percentage of driving time to total working time is a poor factor of performance and one which offers potential for worthwhile improvement but it needs constant monitoring by management to ensure that pre-set standards are maintained. In the case of service-oriented businesses the opposite may apply where driving is the wasteful factor and time spent at customer premises is the productive time element.

7. *Increased number of deliveries per day* – clearly an improved state of productivity will have been achieved if an increase in the number of deliveries which the driver makes in the day is effected. However, this is dependent on a number of factors not least the availability of orders against which deliveries can be made. However, if the orders are available then it requires efficient scheduling to enable the extra deliveries to be made within the driver's permissible working hours. The scheduling will involve planning the journey to ensure that orders are delivered in sequential order according to customer requirements and availability (ie opening and order acceptance times) and to ensure that the route mileage is kept to a minimum to reduce waste travel time.

8. *Improved driving techniques* – as already discussed in Chapter 8, the manner of driving is shown clearly by the chart recordings and therefore it becomes possible to use this as a basis for determining some form of productivity-based payment system. In this case the productivity is in the form of cost savings which undoubtedly result from good driving or conversely a lack of productivity will

take the form of increased costs from poor driving.

9. *Cost savings* – following the points made above about driving techniques as a basis for determining payment schemes, it is useful to consider specifically what cost savings are likely to result from a good driving technique. Considerate driving shows its most immediate effect in fuel consumption which will improve, and quite dramatically so in some instances. For example, a heavy weight vehicle with a high box body running on motorways consumes fuel at a staggering rate when driven at high speed – say 60-70mph which is over the maximum permissible limit anyway – but if the speed was reduced to a more reasonable and consistent range of say 55-60mph then the fuel consumption would improve dramatically without a significant deterioration in journey times.

While this is an extreme example, nevertheless considerable savings would accrue in lower speed operations if a sympathetic driving manner was employed. Along with the savings in fuel, there will be savings in tyre life and in brake lining life plus less tangible but equally valuable savings in repair costs on transmission and suspension systems and the power unit.

In all these areas the driver can play a significant part towards achieving greater efficiency and greater economy; in other words greater productivity – and for his part and his willing contribution he could be rewarded by a payment scheme which reflects the benefits to the fleet operator.

Accident-Free Bonuses

Tachographs are claimed to be able to reduce the incidence of accidents in vehicle fleets as a direct result of the improved driving techniques employed by drivers. Such reductions have obvious benefits for the operator. The cost of repairing damage and renewing paintwork is reduced (especially in minor non-claim bumps), loss of vehicle use is reduced, the hassle of completing forms and generally dealing with insurance claims is reduced with obvious cost savings and finally and most importantly, reduced insurance premiums can be obtained. Again these are good reasons for providing bonus incentives to drivers to improve their driving methods and reduce accidents and minor collisions with other vehicles and stationary objects (posts, pillars, fences, walls, gateways, loading bays, overhanging obstacles, shop blinds and so on). The bonus payment can be related to a points scheme for periods of time without accident/incident or to a reduction in repair costs or reduction in insurance premiums.

11: Tachographs in Transport Planning

Effective use of tachographs and particularly the data extracted by analysis from chart recordings can revolutionise the fleet manager's ability to control and monitor the activities of vehicles and drivers in his charge. More especially it will substantially increase his planning opportunities to achieve more effective and more economic distribution operations.

Prior to the availability of data from tachographs, the amount of worthwhile information about the activities of drivers and vehicles when they were away from base was extremely limited. The driver usually reported verbally any exceptional traffic hold-ups en route and frustrating and time-consuming delays, or contretemps over delivery, at customer premises. But these incidents are not the only things to occur which would inhibit the efficiency of the driver's working day. It is these other 'incidents' (ie matters of speed and distance, delivery and collection times, official breaks and unofficial breaks) which contribute to the inefficiency of the operation and of these the fleet manager knew nothing beyond what he could surmise or what his intuition led him to believe.

It is true that the driver had a statutory record sheet to complete showing the amount of time he was engaged in driving, working and taking breaks, to the nearest quarter of an hour. He may also have completed operating documents showing number and location of deliveries, weights carried, fuel drawn and so on. None of this information, however, was precise in its description or its accuracy of timing, especially that from the record sheet, and it did not tell the manager how the vehicle performed or was treated.

Need for Planning

In view of the many constraints and restrictions placed on fleet operators these days, it is absolutely essential that they have much more knowledge about the activities so that adequate controls and disciplines can be imposed and so that proper advanced planning can take place to ensure efficient operations.

Consider the value of the investment in the vehicle which the driver has in his care, to say nothing of the value of the load which may exceed this many times over and which, in some instances, may also be highly dangerous, particularly susceptible to damage or extremely attractive to thieves. Then there is the high cost of operating the vehicle; high insurance premiums; high repair costs, made worse by the downtime which can be ill-afforded and now increased as a result of tachograph installation and repair; high tyre costs; high fuel costs; drivers' wages, overtime and subsistence expenses which are a substantial element in total costs plus, of course, other factors like depreciation.

With all these items, the transport operating industry is entering a new arena where the costs of today bear little or no relation to those of very few years ago. The problem of vehicle purchase prices affected by high levels of inflation, reductions in the maximum permissible hours which a driver may spend behind the wheel, and many other legislative restrictions have extremely serious cost implications for the fleet operator. But even this is not the whole picture. There is increasing traffic congestion on roads and restriction on inner city parking and loading/unloading. Customers increasingly impose severe, and often inconsiderate, restrictions on delivery time. Yet the possibility of operating and delivering outside normal daytime hours is as far away as ever. This total situation leaves the fleet operator very little scope for reducing costs or planning for increased efficiency. But he must achieve these objectives if he is to survive.

It used to be suggested in many quarters that the transport operating industry in the UK could not afford the tachograph. It is now clear that, in the light of the present state of affairs, it cannot afford to be without the tachograph.

Tachograph Opportunities

Here is an instrument which offers fleet operators an excellent opportunity to look much more closely at their operational planning and at the performance of vehicles and drivers alike. It enables them to ensure that their operations are carried out fully within the law. It enables them to measure the utilisation of both vehicles and drivers against available times or maximum permitted times. It shows where delays are occurring and the true extent of those delays. It shows how vehicles have been treated and the varying skills and techniques of drivers. It will highlight many of the hidden factors surrounding accidents.

With legislation requiring the fitment and use of tachographs, operators are faced with two alternative strategies. The first is to fit the instrument, pay the money and then use it merely to the extent which the law demands. The second is a more constructive approach where the positive benefits which undoubtedly exist with tachographs are sought and the instrument and analysis system become the backbone of an efficient transport fleet planning, control and recording programme. The first option adds cost and aggravation to the operation, the second option makes a valuable contribution and ensures that the operator more than recovers his expenditure on tachograph installation and, in fact, produces either additional savings in cost or other operational benefits.

Driver resistance to the tachograph has not been as widespread or as deeply felt as expected. Consequently, a large proportion of operators have found negotiations with drivers, and certainly with those who do a good day's work within the law and who have nothing to hide, has not been the problem they anticipated. Many operators who have used tachographs for some time have found their drivers to be interested, even enthusiastic, and responsibly disposed towards the instrument. Clearly, such a reaction helps considerably towards the use of tachograph data in planning and control programmes and in the early days of tachograph use some operators reported extremely encouraging benefits to both the driver and the company.

It is obvious that a sensible approach to the subject in human relations terms will pay dividends from the outset whereas any attempt to bludgeon acceptance of the instrument for recording and planning purposes beyond the bare minimum that the law requires will inevitably be doomed to failure. Although it should not need saying, drivers are perceptive and responsible people who will act accordingly given that they have confidence in their employer. Building confidence is, therefore, the first necessary step in a tachograph implementation programme. Only a joint effort by drivers and management will produce the real benefits which tachographs can offer.

Training Needs

Besides the need for joint effort there is also a need for training on both sides. Drivers need to understand what the instrument is, what it does, what the end result looks like and what it all means. They should be able to look at recordings on charts, identify the principal recording areas and interpret in general terms what is indicated. Furthermore, of necessity, the driver needs to know and be trained to remember what actions he must take throughout his work period to produce recordings which comply with the law and which are meaningful to the employer.

The training need applies equally to management and to transport operational and administrative staff. On their shoulders rests the burden of administering the rather more complex aspects of translating chart recordings into usable operating data from which it can be determined whether drivers have complied with the law and which can form the basis of planning and decision making.

Only a relatively small number of operators have become closely involved with tachograph chart analysis; for the remainder the subject of tachograph analysis is new or unknown territory. It is beset with small snags and pitfalls which will take time and effort to overcome – leaving aside the initial problem of legal interpretation of certain aspects of the regulations as discussed in earlier chapters. These difficulties can and will be overcome to the benefit of drivers, of management, of companies and to the industry as a whole. But the path will be a lot easier for those firms who play the game by the obvious ground rules; adopt a positive attitude; recognise the human aspects; organise the necessary training; work together – management with drivers – to achieve the common objective; namely, more cost-effective fleet operations.

Use of Data

Having accepted these philosophies, the question may be asked, how can tachograph-produced data be used in fleet planning and monitoring? The answer is not easy to give because much depends on the nature of the transport operation. Data that is applicable and relevant in one area may be of little or no use in another. For example, it is hardly possible to compare the planning and monitoring involved in multi-drop local delivery operations with that of long-distance trunking. Nevertheless there are certain commonalities in terms of useful data. Consideration of distances travelled and average speeds for example are very different but relevant to both.

The information recorded on a tachograph chart is akin to the information which a work study researcher would produce if he travelled with the vehicle. However, as most managers will know, the day the researcher goes out on a vehicle is the day when the driver claims that everything is different to normal and therefore the observations and timings, he would say, bear no relation to the job as it really exists on a day-to-day basis. Thus the tachograph, once it is fully accepted by the driver and used correctly to produce accurate records, becomes a day-to-day work study 'researcher' providing detailed and reliable data about the job as it does really exist.

Looked at in this light the chart recording can begin to provide a great deal of useful planning information as was described in some detail in Chapter 8 when discussing analysis procedures. It is this information which can be used in planning for more efficient operations. Such planning will revolve around the utilisation of vehicles and the available working time of drivers; around average speed of travel and the amount of 'stop' time for collections and deliveries; around the distances travelled between base and delivery locations and in a whole shift; around the road types and routes followed by the driver; and around the delay time and slack times in the day's schedule.

Trunking Operations

In the case of trunking operations, known average speeds of travel calculated from previous chart recordings will indicate the distance a driver can reasonably accomplish in a shift according to the nature of the route involved. Similarly, previous records of delivery times can be used to determine the likely times for making future deliveries on a pro-rata basis of so many minutes per unit or per parcel or per ton of goods involved.

Analysis of past delays will indicate too the likely extent of delay factors which should be taken into consideration in planning schedules:

So the analysis of a journey plan will comprise:

distance × average speed	=	x hours
delivery of y units at x minutes per unit	=	x hours
average delay factor	=	x hours
official breaks	=	x hours
	total	x hours schedule

Then:

A. Driver's working shift – x hours schedule = slack time in schedule

or

B. Driver's working shift – x hours schedule = overtime in schedule

At this point consideration can be given to the alternative situations A or B. In the case of A the question arises as to whether further work can be added into the schedule without encroaching beyond the driver's legal working limits or in the case of B whether the work schedule can be reduced to bring the operation back to within legal limits.

Conversely, it may be prudent to consider whether value can be added to schedule A by increasing the work to cover the slack period and extend into the next shift (taking account of the cost of night-out subsistence and so on) to make a more cost-effective schedule covering one day and some of the next day.

The ability to plan in advance in this way with some degree of certainty of the end result is a prime benefit to be derived from the use of analysed chart recordings. Without such data the schedule becomes a hit and miss affair with the consequences in the examples given of either a badly under-utilised driver and vehicle working day or an over-utilised day which results in an illegal operation if the driver completes the schedule in one day or unexpected night out if he stops when his time is up plus the fact that the vehicle is not where it is most wanted on the next day.

Other factors can be drawn into this hypothetical schedule. For example, consideration can be given to the effect of increasing the average speed of travel (by reducing stops – not by speeding) and to the effect of reducing delivery time. The former is a matter for negotiation with the driver while the latter is for negotiation with the customer or for consideration of more significant measures.

Viability of Ancillary Equipment

It is at this point that data from tachograph charts can reveal the benefits of vehicle-mounted loading equipment. Although not relevant in all operations, such equipment can provide enormous benefits where it is suitably applicable and the times shown on tachograph chart recordings for loading and delivery can give a good indication of the likely viability of such equipment. For example, the charts for a period of three months for one vehicle may show:

x number of scheduled runs incorporating
y number of loadings and deliveries

Then:
either   A average time per loading and delivery (L & D) $\times$ y
                = total hours L & D
or   B total accumulated hours L & D

Then:
x hours L & D at £x per hour vehicle standing time
      plus   £x per hour driver wage costs
                      = total cost per hour L & D

Then:
Total hours L & D x £x per hour = total cost L & D for 3 months

Then:

Total cost L & D $\times$ 4 = total cost per annum for L & D

Then:

1. Calculate cost of equipment, fitting and downtime
2. Calculate running /repair/depreciation cost of equipment
3. Calculate saving in time by use of equipment
4. Calculate saving in cost by use of equipment

thus:

$$\frac{\text{Original total cost for L \& D}}{\text{Cost of equipment + reduced cost of L \& D}} \times 100 = \% \text{ saving}$$

It was made clear earlier that the potential use of ancillary loading and unloading aids may not exist in which case the above calculation serves no purpose. However, the hypothesis can be extended to consider the utilisation of vehicles rather than just loading and unloading times.

Vehicle Utilisation

Taking a series of analyses across a whole fleet where such factors as running times and distances and loading and delivery times are calculated for the whole fleet, then it becomes possible to consider two things: individual vehicle utilisation and total fleet utilisation:

For example:

$$\frac{\text{Total driving time}}{\text{Total duty time}} \times 100 = \text{x\% utilisation of shift time}$$

or

$$\frac{\text{Total driving time}}{24 \text{ hours}} \times 100 = \text{x\% utilisation of vehicle availability time}$$

However, these calculations relate only to the relationship of driving time to total time, they do not take account of loading and delivery time, but this can be corrected by recalculating as follows:

$$\frac{\text{Total driving plus L \& D time}}{\text{Total duty time}} \times 100 = \text{x\% utilisation of shift time}$$

or

$$\frac{\text{Total driving plus L \& D time}}{24 \text{ hours}} \times 100 = \text{x\% utilisation of vehicle availability time}$$

In either case the important point is to use the available data to establish just how much time is effectively used and how much time is spare and therefore wasted. At some point the calculations may well show that by adding the balance of under-utilised time across a number of vehicles or across the fleet as a whole, this may amount to the operating time of one whole vehicle which, consequently, could be removed from the fleet as surplus capacity. If this can be achieved then real savings will have accrued from the tachograph data.

Multi-drop Operations

Multi-drop local delivery operations are at the other end of the operating spectrum from long-distance trunking but the data from tachograph charts is equally valuable – perhaps even more so. The reason for this is that in such operations the relevant factor of loading time, delivery time and running time have a considerable bearing on the efficiency of the operation. These can become critical items in the quest to schedule more deliveries into drivers' limited working hours and into the ever more restricted acceptance times of retail shop customers. Extraction of data on a regular basis from charts can provide a background of reliable bases on which delivery schedules can be planned to achieve the most efficient delivery patterns.

Taking a typical multi-drop local delivery type chart recording, it is possible to make an analysis of the recorded data as follows:

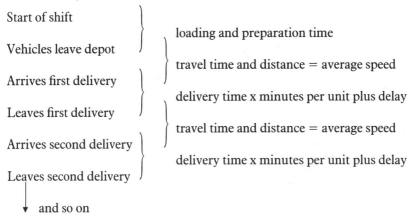

By working through the whole run this way a number of factors become clear as follows:

1. Average travel speed between each delivery.
2. Average travel speed all day.
3. Actual loading and preparation time.
4. Actual delivery time at each drop.
5. Actual delivery time all day.
6. Total of other non-travel, non-delivery times.

Over a period these individual travel times will change in relation to the time of day, day of week and week of year; in summer and winter; in good weather and bad; when mornings and afternoons are light and dark.

The delivery times will also change with fluctuating order sizes; with different drivers who delay longer at one place than another driver. Also times will change when regular drivers are replaced by temporary stand-ins and a considerable reduction in efficiency (ie increase in time) may be expected. But sometimes the expected becomes the unexpected when a temporary driver satisfactorily completes a route in less time or over less distance than the regular driver.

With a breakdown of average running times and individual delivery times at customers' premises plus a knowledge of loading and preparation times it becomes possible to consider the efficiency of existing schedules and the possibilities offered by changing the schedules, by juggling the sequence of deliveries on the route, by juggling the allocation of deliveries to particular routes. The whole exercise can be plotted graphically to see the effects of change against existing operations as follows:

MAXIMUM DRIVER SHIFT – x hours

1	Loading	Travel	Delivery	Delay	Spare

2	Longer loading	Travel	Deliveries	Delay	

Reduced spare time↵

3	Loading	Travel	Deliveries	Delay

Note: Delay contingency reduced and no spare time in route

4	Loading	Travel	Deliveries

Note: Route extended too far – beyond driver limit

Therefore schedule 2 is the best compromise, keeping spare or slack time in the schedule to a minimum, encompassing the maximum possible number of deliveries with reduced travel time.

This situation can also be illustrated as follows:

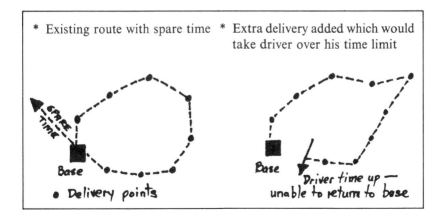

Figure 11.1 *Scheduling for greater efficiency*

With the ability to plot schedules in this way using known travel and delivery times from tachograph chart data it is possible to consider the implications in advance of adding deliveries to a schedule or deducting deliveries from an established schedule. It is also possible to change vehicles or drivers systematically to identify the effects of all these variable factors.

Route Planning

Another possibility in planning terms is determination of the route itself. From a chart recording the route used by the driver can be approximately identified in terms of his use of minor roads, urban roads, trunk roads and motorways. The difference between driving on such roads shows both in the driving manner and the speeds travelled. Two alternative situations which may arise are, firstly, excessive use of motorways by the driver which may cut down on total time (but will increase the cost of running because of the high fuel consumption over a greater distance) in reaching his destination or, secondly, insufficient use of motorways which saves on fuel and other costs because of reduced mileage but which increase travel time to the destination. It is a question of deciding the priorities, speed or cost and instructing the driver accordingly.

Cost Control

With the ability to examine the use of vehicles as described from tachograph chart analysis it becomes possible to relate cost factors to individual vehicles. For a start the tachograph provides a more accurate recording of distance than a speedometer and because of its greater reliability and the legal pressure on keeping it in working order, overall it provides a more reliable record of distance. Thus with accurate distance records, fuel consumption can be calculated with greater efficiency, so too can tyre and brake lining life. Total vehicle operating costs can also be calculated with greater accuracy and costs can be related to actual usage of vehicles (ie the hours worked in a day; the hours of travel time and standing time in a day). By constantly plotting utilisation factors and relating costs the fleet operator will find that the tachograph gives him greater control in general terms across the whole fleet and specifically in the case of spare vehicles and where there is unauthorised use of vehicles.

Spare Vehicle Use

In the case of spare vehicles it is common practice for traffic schedulers to spread work across the whole fleet rather than endeavour to contain it among fewer vehicles each of which achieves a higher level of utilisation and leaving some vehicles not utilised at all. Such a situation could be forced into existence by withdrawing some vehicles from service but while spare vehicles remain available there is no pressure on the schedulers to seek better utilisation of fewer vehicles or to be more selective in which vehicles they use for each particular task. Similarly, by spreading the total work load across a larger number of vehicles it becomes easier to give or fulfil specific delivery promises as to time of arrival and so on. In a much tighter operating situation through the availability of fewer vehicles this would not be possible to anywhere near the same extent without careful planning. And it is worth remembering that scheduling around specific delivery times results in inefficient planning and therefore more costly operations so the more that such constraints can be avoided the greater the possibility of achieving efficient planning, better vehicle utilisation and more cost-effective operations.

Unauthorised Use of Vehicles

If tachograph chart recordings are carefully analysed and compared to operating sheets, any unauthorised use of vehicles and unauthorised stopping will be highlighted. Remembering what high costs are involved in vehicle running it will be seen to be important to eliminate any unnecessary running of vehicles.

Special Deliveries

A point that chart recordings will also reveal very effectively is the detail of special or urgent deliveries which frequently occur in operations, mainly at the customer's request. It has been hard to identify the true costs of such requests in the past but the chart will show the time involved in loading, travelling, delivery and returning to base as well as the precise distance covered so that an accurate assessment of cost and of effect on other operations can be made.

Conclusion

From these examples it will be seen that use of tachograph chart data provides plenty of opportunity for more efficient planning and costing of vehicle operations. It also provides the opportunity to improve vehicle utilisation and possibly reduce the number of vehicles required and can make a worthwhile contribution toward selection of vehicles or equipment which achieve better results in terms of delivery time and faster vehicle turnround. However, these benefits will only result from consistent and accurate analysis of chart data. In the same way that work study records for many years provided the yardstick for efficiency monitoring, now the tachograph can fulfil the same role more efficiently and at less cost.

12: Chart Recordings in Practice

The author has seen a great number of charts produced by drivers as their official record. Many of these charts would satisfy legal requirements but with still only limited knowledge among fleet operators about tachographs and the rules governing their use, it is inevitable that quite a large proportion of such charts would be incorrectly completed and inaccurate in detail, besides, in certain cases, reflecting obvious instances of contravention of the drivers' hours law. Some too, bear evidence of driver interference with the chart, or the recording mechanism of the instrument. Since it is useful for fleet managers to be fully familiar with the characteristics of such errors, omissions and tamperings, a collection of genuine charts showing a number of specific examples of such instances has been gathered for illustration in this chapter.

It should be noted that the references here are not to compliance with the drivers' hours law which, with the older charts, in any case, differed from that of the present day, but rather to irregularities of recordings. It should also be noted that not all the examples illustrated are evidence of driver interference or deliberate attempts to falsify charts. Some arise from pure ignorance of the manner in which tachographs should be operated, others from malfunctions of the instrument itself. Further, since it was not possible to double check on the circumstances of each instance illustrated, it is possible that different explanations or variations on the explanation given may be possible.

Overrun Recordings

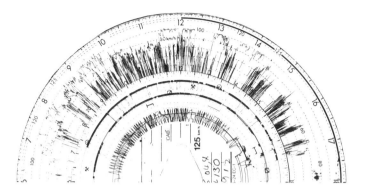

Overrun recording. The chart appears to have been in the instrument for at least 72 hours and driving has been done with the switch in the ◻ mode

This one was left in longer!

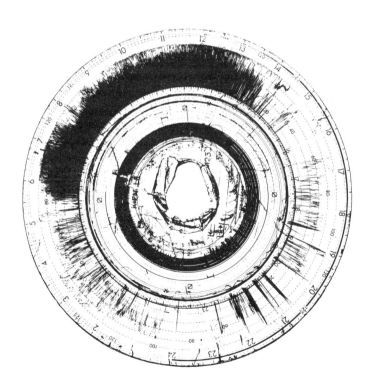

Jammed Clocks

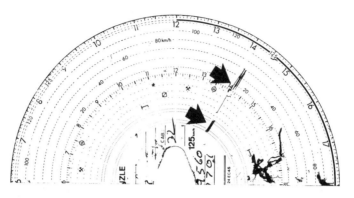

Clock jammed at 14.05

*Clock jammed at 06.25 and again
at 08.20 to 08.25—but then
it appears to work
properly!*

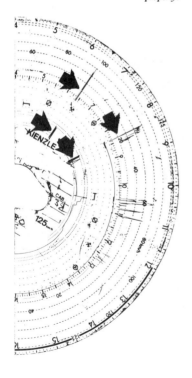

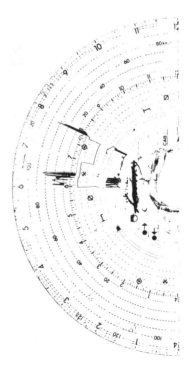

Another jammed recording

Clock faulty at 06.45 to 07.00. Also other marks at 08.40 (speed only) and at 10.05 and 10.20 (speed and distance trace)

Clock jammed at 06.30

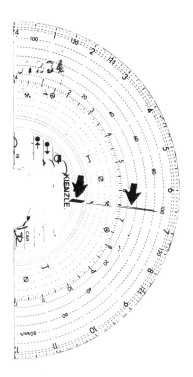

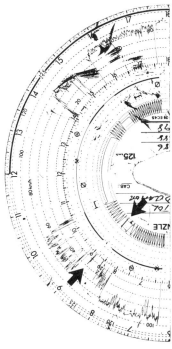

Tachograph opened at 08.40. Vehicle driven at 08.50 to 08.55 with clock stopped

Tachograph Faults

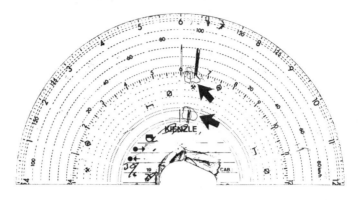

Trouble at 06.00 to 06.35. The circular recordings were made by the styli

More strange circles created by styli when the chart stopped rotating. Note damage to centre hole

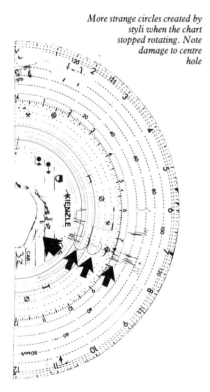

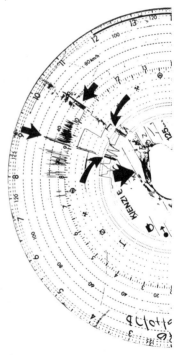

Tachograph fault from 09.05 when clock first jammed until approx. 10.30 when chart removed. Note damage to centre field again

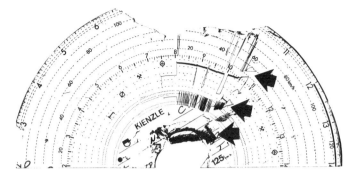

Another example of damage to chart and recordings. Note centre field again

Faulty Recordings

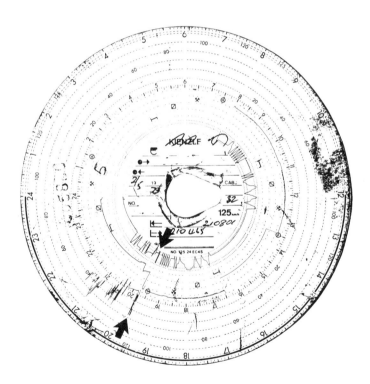

Faulty recording of time groups from 08.00 to 19.30 when vehicle driven. Distance trace appears normal but speed trace is missing. From 19.45 when chart had been removed and re-inserted, rotation of chart has been inhibited and recording damaged

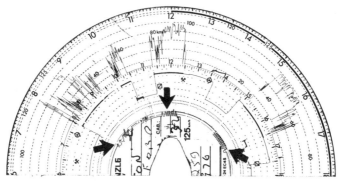

Fault on distance recording

*Fault on driving trace—the
broad running line
has not been
recorded*

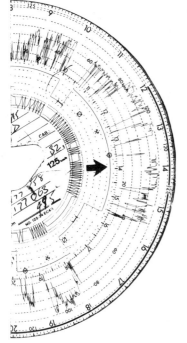

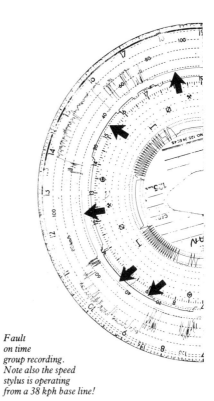

*Fault
on time
group recording.
Note also the speed
stylus is operating
from a 38 kph base line!*

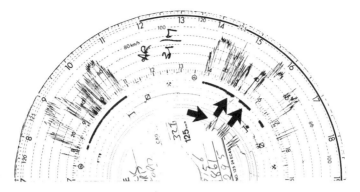

Vehicle running trace is not sharply defined especially from 14.50 onwards. No distance trace has been recorded until approximately 14.50 when the running trace deteriorates

Instrument Openings

Example of instrument openings at 11.30 and 15.30 on first rotation of the chart. Note also minor opening at 11.15

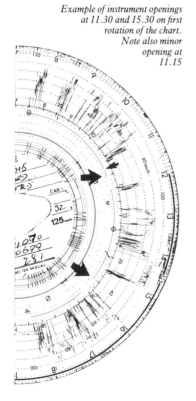

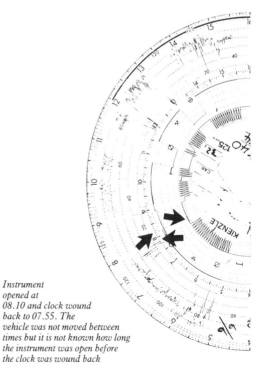

Instrument opened at 08.10 and clock wound back to 07.55. The vehicle was not moved between times but it is not known how long the instrument was open before the clock was wound back

Inspection of Charts

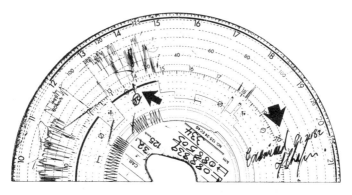

A frequent question is how will an enforcement officer indicate that he has examined a chart. This example shows how it may be done

Interference with Recordings

Accident Recordings

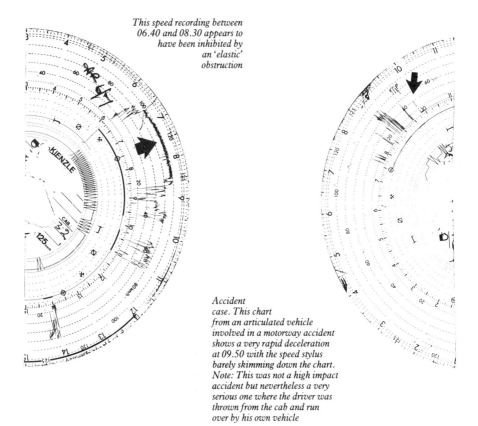

This speed recording between 06.40 and 08.30 appears to have been inhibited by an 'elastic' obstruction

Accident case. This chart from an articulated vehicle involved in a motorway accident shows a very rapid deceleration at 09.50 with the speed stylus barely skimming down the chart. Note: This was not a high impact accident but nevertheless a very serious one where the driver was thrown from the cab and run over by his own vehicle

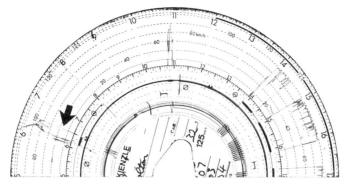

The driver reported an accident at 06.30. The speed recording shows a very rapid halt. Subsequently the chart was left in the instrument for a number of rotations

False Recordings

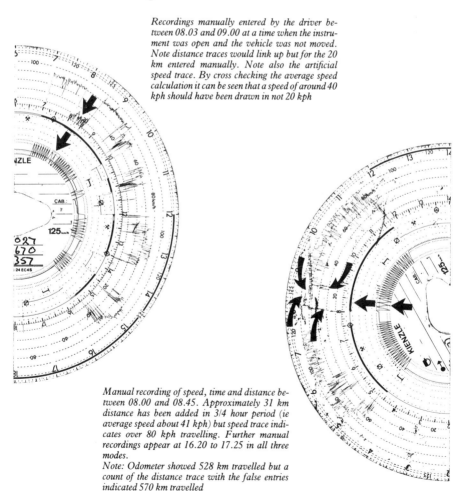

Recordings manually entered by the driver between 08.03 and 09.00 at a time when the instrument was open and the vehicle was not moved. Note distance traces would link up but for the 20 km entered manually. Note also the artificial speed trace. By cross checking the average speed calculation it can be seen that a speed of around 40 kph should have been drawn in not 20 kph

Manual recording of speed, time and distance between 08.00 and 08.45. Approximately 31 km distance has been added in 3/4 hour period (ie average speed about 41 kph) but speed trace indicates over 80 kph travelling. Further manual recordings appear at 16.20 to 17.25 in all three modes.

Note: Odometer showed 528 km travelled but a count of the distance trace with the false entries indicated 570 km travelled

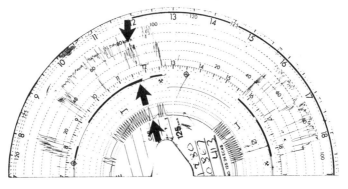

Manual recording on all three modes from 11.30 to 12.10

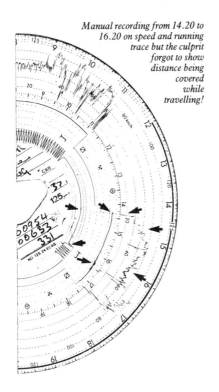

Manual recording from 14.20 to 16.20 on speed and running trace but the culprit forgot to show distance being covered while travelling!

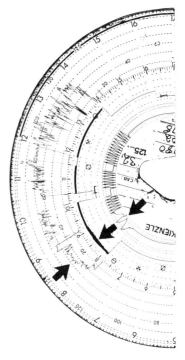

Manual entry 07.50 to 09.05. Again average speed does not fit in with the speed and distance recording

Strange Openings

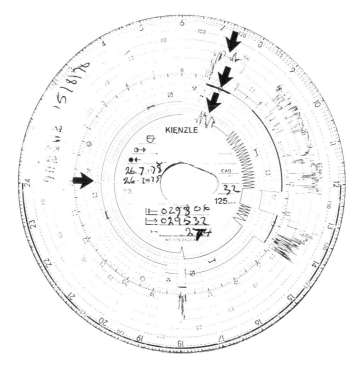

Manual entry of speed, time (ie travel) and distance from 07.00 to 07.55. Also, who opened the instrument for a period from 24.00 to 00.10?

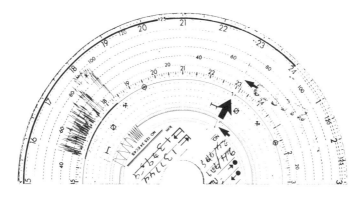

Curiosity would require an explanation of the recordings commencing at 23.00 for 3 km, with the instrument then opened for about five minutes while the vehicle was moving

Another case of curious vehicle movements recorded by automatic tachograph at 22.15 and 22.40 (different firm to item above)

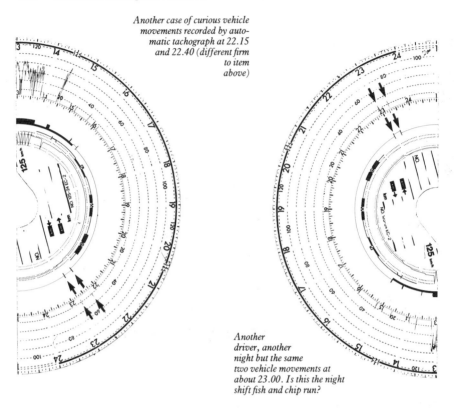

Another driver, another night but the same two vehicle movements at about 23.00. Is this the night shift fish and chip run?

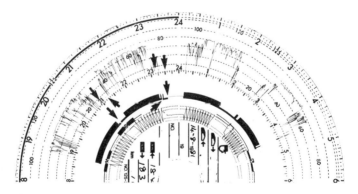

Instrument opened at 20.55, vehicle was driven and clock turned back to 20.58. Also note speed stylus base line has moved up from 20.58 until 23.10 when instrument was opened again (and again at 23.31). Then it returned to the normal base line

Typical Recordings

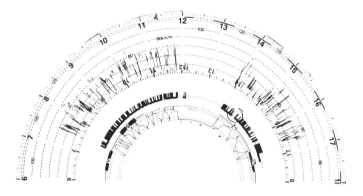

Typical stop-start delivery operation recording by an automatic tachograph

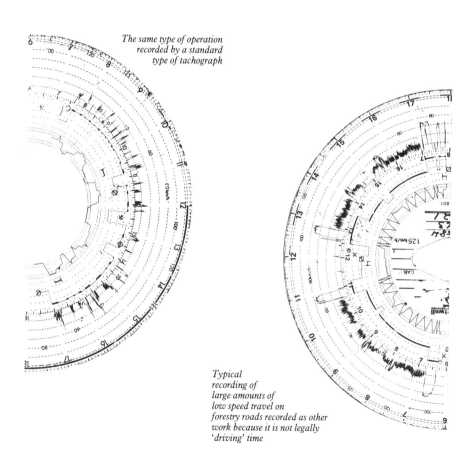

The same type of operation recorded by a standard type of tachograph

Typical recording of large amounts of low speed travel on forestry roads recorded as other work because it is not legally 'driving' time

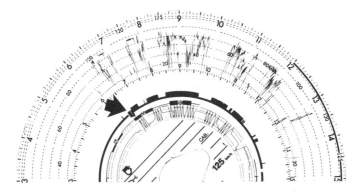

Bad recording at 06.25. Instrument face probably not properly closed (automatic instrument)

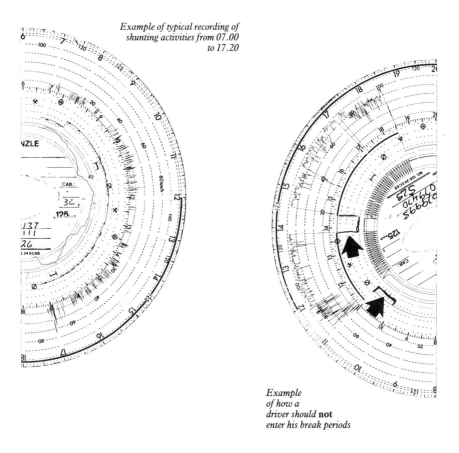

Example of typical recording of shunting activities from 07.00 to 17.20

*Example of how a driver should **not** enter his break periods*

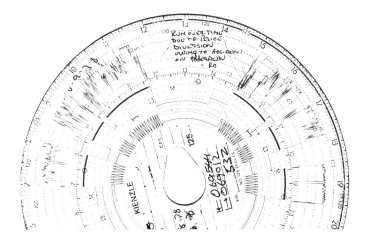

Example of how driver can sensibly record legitimate delays which take him over his time

13: How Tachograph Law Applies in the UK

The fitment and use of tachographs in goods and passenger vehicles in the United Kingdom is governed by Part VI of the Transport Act 1968, EC Regulation 3821/85 (see Appendix I) and The Passenger and Goods Vehicles (Recording Equipment) Regulations 1979 (as amended).

Most of the practical operating requirements which concern vehicles users and drivers are contained in the Community Recording Equipment Regulations (ie EC Regulation 3821/85) rather than in the Transport Act or the Recording Equipment regulations mentioned above. These regulations specify the requirements for the instrument itself, its installation and calibration and the tolerances within which it must operate, and the technical requirements for the recording methods and the charts (ie record sheets) themselves.

Additionally, the regulations spell out in detail the individual responsibilities of the employer of the driver and of the driver himself. These responsibilities constitute the principal legal requirements for the use of tachographs and the purpose of this chapter is to explain these requirements in detail. This information will be useful reading also for European readers because for all practical purposes the application of the EC regulations is the same in each European state as in the UK.

In order to comply with the regulations in total, three particular aspects have to be observed as follows:

1. The tachograph instrument and its installation must conform to the technical specification set out in Annex 1 to EC Regulation 3821/85 (see Appendix I).
2. The complete installation must be calibrated and sealed in accordance with the requirements of Annex 1 mentioned above.
3. The instrument must be used to produce official records in accordance with the regulations with both parties observing their respective share of the responsibilities;
   (a) responsibilities of the employer and owner driver
   (b) responsibilities of the driver.

The items under headings 1 and 2 are dealt with in detail in Chapter 2.
The third item is dealt with in detail here.

Compliance with the Law

Before describing the individual responsibilities in detail it is important to point out that both employer and driver alike have similar responsibilities for ensuring that the law is fully complied with. This means a need for strict observance of the driving hours rules and record-keeping requirements. Failure by either party to comply or to ensure compliance will result in severe penalties – financial ones imposed by the courts plus operational ones imposed in the UK by the Licensing Authority against both the employer's operator's licences and the driver's HGV driving licences (see Chapter 14).

Employers of goods and passenger vehicle drivers have an overriding responsibility to ensure that their employees are fully aware of the requirements of the law in respect of these matters; that they know what they must do or must not do to comply; that they know *how* to comply and finally that as a matter of regular course the employer checks to ensure that the law is being complied with. In other words they must take all possible steps to ensure that the law is complied with. Anything less than 'all possible steps' could leave open the opportunity for a court to say that an employer could and should have taken more steps than he did to convince employees of the need for acting legally and thus the employer could stand convicted of such charges as 'failing to cause...' records, or proper records, to be kept.

Responsibilities of Employer

It is the responsibility of the employer of the driver to ensure that the following points are observed. In the case of an owner-driver he carries both the responsibilities of the employer and the driver. In the case of drivers hired from agencies then it is the vehicle user (ie the temporary employer of the driver) who must accept these responsibilities. If vehicles are provided to a firm on a contract basis with drivers supplied then it is the contract hire firm not the hirer who carries the responsibilities.

The employer's individual responsibilities are as follows:

Correct Use
1. Ensure that in all respects the driver knows how to use his tachograph and how to complete charts and that he actually does so properly.
   He must be provided with a key to open the instrument.

Correct Charts
2. Obtain the correct and most suitable type of charts. Not all charts are interchangeable between makes and models of tachograph and a variety of alternative charts are on the market.

Issue of Charts
3. Issue appropriate supplies to drivers. The legislation does not specify any limits but in general terms at least three charts would be needed at the start of each day as follows:
   (a) one to be the record for the day
   (b) one spare to be carried in case the first chart is seized by an enforcement officer (see p 145).

(c) one further spare to be carried in case either of the other two charts becomes too dirty or damaged to be used.

This problem becomes complicated when drivers are likely to switch during the day from vehicles fitted with one make of tachograph to those fitted with a different make. In these circumstances he would need sufficient clean spare charts of either a universal type or of the appropriate individual type to cover each make of instrument to be used.

Collection of Charts

4. Once charts have been used and completed by drivers and retained for the minimum statutory period (see p 147) they must be returned to the employer within 21 days unless there are special reasons why this is not possible (see p 138). *This 21-day limit for the return of charts is a UK requirement only and is not a specific requirement of the EC regulations.*

Checking of Charts

5. When charts have been returned by the driver, there is a requirement for them to be checked* to ensure that the law has been complied with. In particular, it is suggested that the following points are observed:

(a) A chart has been completed for the day.
(b) The chart is properly completed in respect of;
   i centre field information
   ii use of activity mode switch to ensure proper recordings of time
   iii any necessary manual entries relating to changes of vehicle
   iv any other manual entries relating to working activities.
(c) The driving hours rules have been observed in respect of;
   i daily spreadover (ie has not encroached into daily rest time)
   ii total daily driving
   iii continuous driving periods
   iv break periods
   v daily rest periods.
(d) The weekly limits have been observed as follows by aggregating information from daily charts;
   i weekly driving (ie in 7 consecutive days)
   ii total two-weekly driving (ie in 14 consecutive days)
   iii total weekly rest.

Note: A summary of the EC driving hours law is given in Appendix III

* NB: There is a requirement under Article 16 (2) of EC Regulation 3820/85 (which deals with the drivers' hours law) for employers to 'make periodic checks to ensure that the provisions of the two regulations† have been complied with'.
   † (ie 3820/85 – hours law and 3821/85 – tachographs).

Retention of Charts

6. Retain charts available for inspection by the enforcement authorities for a period of twelve months.

Responsibilities of Driver

Keeping Charts Clean

1. Keep new and used charts clean and free from damage. If a partially used chart is damaged, a new chart should be used to replace it and at the end of the day both charts should be securely attached together to comprise the day's record.

Completion of Centre Field

2. On a day when a vehicle to which the regulations apply is driven* complete the centre field of the chart:
   (a) At the beginning of the shift;
       i surname and christian name (not initials)
       ii place of starting work
       iii date on which shift started
       iv vehicle registration number
       v odometer reading at the start of the first journey.
   (b) At the end of the shift:
       i place of finishing work
       ii date on which shift finished (ie day-shift drivers will have entered the same date twice which confirms that he worked a days shift as shown by recording while conversely night-shift drivers will have entered two consecutive dates)
       iii odometer readings at the completion of the last journey of the day.
   (c) During the shift (if any change of vehicle);
       i time of taking control of replacement vehicle (by 24-hour clock)
       ii registration number of vehicle
       iii odometer readings for the vehicle.

   This information must be repeated for each vehicle driven during the shift.

   * An important point in the application of the tachograph rules is that charts do not have to be produced by drivers on days when they work for their employer but do not drive a vehicle to which the regulations apply (ie days in the yard or warehouse or driving light vehicles which are outside the rules).

Other Non-Statutory Information

Some charts have space for recording other data which is not required by law. The principal items are as follows:

(a) By subtraction the total distance driven with each vehicle. There is no legal requirement to complete this

(b) 'CAB' entry requirements. This is intended to be used to indicate whether the vehicle has a sleeper cab or a non-sleeper cab which is relevant if the vehicle is operated by two crew members who are taking advantage of the reduced daily rest period requirements applicable in such circumstances. Where appropriate the entry can be made voluntarily as follows;

S   – sleeper cab

X   – non-sleeper cab

or

N-S   – non-sleeper cab

(c) Vehicle weight. A small letter 't' is printed on some charts against which the driver may write the maximum permissible weight of his vehicle (eg '38t')

It must be stressed that these entries are *not* part of the legal requirements.

Clock to be Right

3. Make sure the tachograph clock is 'right' both in hours and minutes and in the right 12-hour section on the chart (so the shift looks as though it starts AM not PM or vice versa).

Note 1: The regulations do not state how accurate the clock setting must be, only that it must accord with 'the official time in the country of registration of the vehicle'.

Note 2: When travelling on international journeys the time on the clock must agree with the official time in the country of registration of the vehicle (this can cause problems in Europe when the difference with Britain applies – especially when British Summer Time is in operation – because local gendarmerie may have a tendency to overlook the difference and expect the clock to be correct to local time).

Note 3: Normally the clock will retain its set time and only when the battery has been disconnected for repairs or service work to be carried out on the vehicles is it likely to be necessary for the driver to have to move the clock to show the correct time.

Activity Mode Switches

4. Operate the Activity Mode Switches on the instrument as necessary to record

(a) Driving

(b) Other work

(c) Breaks and daily rest periods.

The switch must be turned at the beginning of each new activity – especially breaks – because the readings cannot be ' wound back' to cover up the fact that the switch was not turned when it should have been.

Failure to turn the switch at the correct time is an offence (failing to keep a proper record and if break periods are not properly recorded the charge could be failing to comply with the drivers' hours regulations).

Crossed Hammers

Although the crossed hammers symbol appears on all tachographs there is no legal requirement that it should be used unless required by national regulations in EC member states – it is not necessary in the UK. Other work activities are recorded normally by using the rectangle with the diagonal line. However, having said that there is no legal requirement to use the symbol, it may be used on a

voluntary basis given that drivers co-operate by using the switch at the appropriate times.

Examples of some possible uses for the crossed hammers symbol are as follows:

(a) To record driving on site (off the public highway) which counts as work
time not driving time. If this course is followed then it would be helpful for
the driver to note on the chart that 'driving against crossed hammers is
driving on site' or words to this effect. Failure to make such a note may
result in questions from enforcement officers who may query why the normal driving symbol was not used. It is perfectly legal to do what is suggested here but the danger is that it can be misconstrued by enforcement
staffs and misused by drivers to gain extra driving time in the day.

(b) To differentiate between collections and deliveries on the same route or
journey

(c) To differentiate between deliveries to 'own' outlets and outside customers
where mixed orders are on the vehicle

(d) To identify delays at delivery points in general or at particular places.

Automatic Tachographs

On automatic-type instruments, there is no steering wheel symbol and thus no
requirement for the driver to select or move the switch from driving when setting off and when stopping. The instrument automatically records these activities and continues to record driving while the vehicle is moving. When the
vehicle stops the instrument reverts back to recording the activity at which the
switch is currently pointing (ie crossed hammers, other work, break or rest
period).

Continuous Records

5. Ensure that a continuous record is made. This entails keeping a watch on the
speedometer needle, odometer and clock to ensure that they are working correctly. This includes making sure that a chart has been put in the instrument
and it is the right way up:

(a) On certain makes of instrument an apperture is provided in the face which
can be illuminated by pushing a button and through which the driver can
see a section of the chart exposed.

(b) On Lucas Kienzle instruments a red warning light system is provided
which illuminates if charts are not in place or a fault occurs in the
recording.

Manual Entries

6. There are many sets of circumstances when the tachograph cannot make a
recording so the driver is required by law to make a manual record of his activities on the chart. The principal times when manual recordings would need to
be made are as follows:

(a) If the tachograph breaks down during a journey, the driver should remove
the chart and continue to manually record his further driving, duty and

break period times for the rest of that day. If the instrument cannot be repaired immediately and the vehicle is required for use for subsequent days, then the driver should make a manual recording on a fresh chart for each day.

Remember a tachograph failure is not an acceptable excuse for not keeping records.

(b) If there is no vehicle available or the driver is away from his vehicle for part of the day then the relevant periods of activity time (ie duty or breaks) must be recorded manually on the chart. For example from clocking on until a vehicle becomes available; during the day between journeys; between changing vehicles; from completing the last journey of the day and clocking off.

(c) If the driver takes his statutory break away from the vehicle at a time when the vehicle may be driven by other people (loaders, yardmen, shunters, garage staff for example).

(d) If the vehicle is likely to be used or moved at night while the driver is taking his daily rest, or if he is likely to start work later on the second day than the first then the daily rest period should be recorded manually rather than leave the chart in the instrument overnight when such activities would put unwanted recordings on the chart or these would be an overlap of recording.

(e) Other manual entries would include notes about the date a chart was last made and the reason for an absence of charts for certain days.

Retention of Charts

7. Retain in his possession used charts as follows:
   (a) charts for current week plus
   (b) chart for the last day of the previous week in which he drove.

The driver must produce these charts to an enforcement officer on request. Normally, the enforcement staffs will sign the chart to justify the gap in the recording but if they do not do so the driver should ask them to note the time and sign the chart.

After retaining the charts for the relevant period mentioned above they must be returned to the employer within 21 days (UK only requirement).

Calibration Plaque

8. The driver must allow an authorised examiner to see the tachograph calibration plaque which is fitted either inside the instrument or in the cab somewhere near to the instrument. The plaque should be intact and have a valid date on it (see p 37).

Driver Check List

The original version of this check list was produced by the author in 1981 to act as a pocket reminder to drivers of what to do in order to operate tachographs successfully and legally.

AT START OF SHIFT
Check:
Have you got at least 3 clean charts with you?
Have you got the current week's charts with you and the one for your last driving day?

BEFORE DRIVING
Complete Centre Field of chart:
 christian name and surname
 date of commencing shift
 place of starting work
 vehicle registration number
 odometer reading

Make any manual entries on chart as necessary:
 daily rest period from 0001 hours to commencing shift
 working time from start of shift until vehicle available

Put chart in instrument
Make sure clock is set to the correct 12 hours (ie am/pm). Adjust if necessary

Make sure chart is securely located in instrument

Close face of instrument and make sure it is secure (otherwise recordings will not be made)

Turn activity mode switch to appropriate symbol:

.... driving .... other work .... break/rest

DURING DAY
Turn activity mode switch to record changes of activity

Observe that instrument continues to work correctly:
 speedometer needle
 odometer rotating
 clock indicator rotating

Take occasional brief (5-10 second) look at the chart to ensure recordings are being made
Make manual note on chart of any unforeseen delays (accidents, breakdowns, etc) which may cause you to exceed permitted time limits

WHEN TAKING BREAK
If vehicle will not be moved while break is being taken:
 turn switch to record break on chart

If vehicle is likely to be moved by other people during break:
 remove chart and make manual record of break period

WHEN LEAVING VEHICLE
At end of driving record further activities on chart:
 further working time
 end of shift time
 rest period from end of shift to 2400 hours

Complete remainder of Centre Field:
    place where shift ends
    date of ending shift
    odometer reading
    by subtraction – total distance travelled (in km)

WHEN CHANGING VEHICLES
Take chart out of instrument and take to next vehicle

Enter details of every vehicle on chart:
    time of changeover
    new vehicle registration number
    odometer readings
    total distance travelled (in km)

Manually record activities between changing vehicles

Insert chart in instrument and record activities

...............driving ....other work ....break/rest

IF TACHOGRAPH BREAKS DOWN DURING SHIFT
Remove chart as soon as possible
Record remainder of shift activities manually on chart
Report failure on return to depot or as soon as possible

IF YOU ARE STOPPED DURING SHIFT
Allow authorised examiner to see:
    current week's charts
    last chart from previous driving week
    calibration plaque in instrument

Ask examiner to sign chart and note time of examination

If chart is impounded ask for receipt giving details from chart:
    date
    vehicle number
    details of working times

IF CHART BECOMES DAMAGED
Replace with new chart and attach damaged and replacement charts together to
    make complete record of shift activity

CHECK AT END OF SHIFT
Is chart fully completed for shift?

Have breaks been recorded correctly?

Are all gaps in recordings covered by manual entries or by other explanations?

AFTER RETAINING CHARTS
Return to company after retaining as required by law but no later than 21 days after
use

REMINDERS

Failure to:
> make proper record
> return charts after use

are offences for which heavy penalties can be imposed

It is a very serious offence to:
> make false entries on charts
> interfere with clock or other workings of instrument

Report lost charts

Report instrument defects

© *David Lowe 1989*
This check list is strictly copyright

14: Offences, Penalties, Defences, Enforcement Powers and Legal Proceedings in the UK

The offences which may be committed under the tachograph regulations and the penalties which will be imposed upon conviction for such offences are covered by the regulations described in Appendices I and III. So too are the powers of the police and other authorities in respect of enforcement of the regulations. However, it is useful to set out the details again in this separate Appendix for ease of reference:

Offences and Penalties

If any person uses, causes or permits to be used on a road a vehicle to which the 1968 Transport Act section 97 applies and:

1. The vehicle is not fitted with recording equipment which has been installed in accordance with EC Regulation 3821/85;
   or
2. recording equipment which has been installed in the vehicle in accordance with Regulation 3821/85 and which complies with those requirements is not used as required by the regulations (Articles 14 to 16), an offence is committed and that person shall be liable to a fine not exceeding £1,000 on summary conviction.
3. If an employed driver fails without reasonable excuse, to return any record sheet to his 'first' employer within 21 days of its completion;
   or
4. If a driver has two or more employers (who employ him to drive goods or passenger vehicles to which the regulations apply) and he fails to notify them of the name and address of each other, he commits an offence under section 97A of the Transport Act 1968 for which he can be fined on summary conviction.
5. If an employer fails, without reasonable excuse, to ensure that drivers comply with these requirements, he commits an offence for which he can be fined on summary conviction.
6. Any person who obstructs an enforcement officer in the exercise of his powers to enter any vehicle and inspect the recording equipment or from entering premises, commits an offence under section 99 (4) of the Transport Act 1968 for which he can be fined on summary conviction.

7. Any person who makes, or causes to be made, any record sheet kept or carried for the purpose of Regulation 3821/85 which he knows to be false, or with intent to deceive, alters or causes to be altered, any such record or entry, he commits an offence under section 99(5) of The Transport Act 1968 for which he can be fined on summary conviction or imprisoned for up to two years on indictment.

Other Penalties

It is also important to note that where such a conviction is made, under other legislation an Operator's licence or a Heavy Goods Vehicle Driver's Licence could be placed in jeopardy since it is a condition of both these licences that the holder must conform to the law on drivers' hours and record keeping (including the fitment and use of tachographs) among other things.

Statutory Defences

The regulations allow certain statutory defences to be put forward in respect of offences committed.

1. A conviction will not be made under item 1 above if it can be shown that at the relevant time the vehicle was travelling to a place to have a tachograph fitted; or
2. If the tachograph was installed but not working, if it can be proved to the court that it had not been reasonably practicable for the equipment to be repaired by an approved fitter or workshop (ie tachograph centre) 'as soon as circumstances permit' and that in the meantime written records were being kept by the driver; or
3. If any seal on the installation is not intact, if it can be proved to the Court that:
   (a) breaking or removal of the seal could not be avoided
   (b) it had not been reasonably practicable for the seal to be replaced by an approved fitter or workshop (ie tachograph centre) 'as soon as circumstances permit'
   and
   (c) the equipment was still being used as required by the regulations (ie Articles 14 to 16 of EC Regulation 3821/85).

Practical Defences

From a practical viewpoint, advantage of the defences outlined can be taken provided that certain positive steps are taken.

In the case of the tachograph failure during a journey, the driver may continue that journey as planned so long as he continues to make a manual recording of his driving and working activities for the rest of that journey or that day. In referring to the term 'journey' this could be a single journey of an hour to two duration, it could be a whole day journey, or it could be a journey lasting several days. There is no legal requirement that the driver should abandon the journey, return to base or even drive around searching for a tachograph centre unless he cannot return to base within seven days (in which case by the seventh day he must get the installation repaired en route).

However, once the vehicle returns to base (or after a maximum of seven days from the date of breakdown – according to Article 16 of EC Regulation 3821/85), it should not be used again until the tachograph installation has been repaired and re-sealed or re-calibrated at an approved tachograph workshop. It is at this point that arrangements should be made for an appointment with the tachograph centre. If an immediate or 'next day' appointment can be made, all is well. If, however, because of the volume of work, a shortage of spare parts supplies, or the centre cannot offer an early appointment then it is in order to continue to use the vehicle under the protection of the defence described above provided certain points are observed:

1. It must be possible to prove to the satisfaction of a court that a definite booking was made to have the installation repaired 'as soon as circumstances permit'. Copies of appointment cards, letters confirming the booking or official repair orders would appear to suffice for this purpose.
2. Drivers must continue without fail to make manual recordings on a chart of their driving, working, break period and daily rest times every day they drive the vehicle with the tachograph not working.
3. The driver must remember that if it is the speedometer function which is defective, while the above defence protects him against having a non-working tachograph there is no defence for exceeding *any* speed limit.

Seven-day Rule

The seven-day rule referred to above which is contained in the EC regulations is only applicable where the vehicle cannot or does not return to base within this time (ie one week). If the vehicle does return to base before this time then the legal requirement is merely to have the installation put back into legally acceptable order 'as soon as circumstances permit'.

Enforcement Powers

Reference has been made earlier to the powers of enforcement staff in regard to the inspection of records but it is worth repeating the details here since they are relevant to this section. Under Part VI of the Transport Act 1968 (section 99) authorised examiners are given certain powers in connection with the enforcement of the drivers' hours and record-keeping requirements of the Act and any relevant regulations made under the Act.

Inspection of Equipment and Records

An authorised examiner may at any time enter any vehicle which comes within the scope of the regulations and inspect any recording equipment (ie tachograph) installed in it. He may further inspect and copy any record sheet (ie tachograph chart) on the vehicle on which a record has been made either by the tachograph or by the driver. While such inspection and copying is carried out he has the right to detain the vehicle. Such an examiner may also, at any reasonable time (depending on the circumstances of the case), enter any premises on which he has reason to believe that a vehicle to which the regulations apply is kept or any record sheets are to be found. He may inspect any vehicle found and inspect and copy any record sheets which he finds there.

Production of Records
An authorised examiner may require any person to produce and permit him to inspect and copy any record sheet (ie tachograph chart) which that person is required to be able to produce, or retain, as follows under EC Regulation 3821/85.

1. Crew members must be able to produce records (Article 15 [7]).
2. Employers must retain records (Article 14 [2]).

If the person referred to above is also the owner of the vehicle (by definition this must include the 'user' if the vehicles are operated on a hired, contract hired or leased arrangement), then the examiner may serve notice in writing to that person that record sheets shall be produced at the Traffic Area office within a period of time specified in the notice. The Traffic Area office must be that which is specified in the notice and the period of time must be not less than ten days from the service of the notice.

Seizure of Records
If an authorised examiner has reason to believe that any person has made or has caused to be made (ie by encouraging or directing another person to make) any record or entry on a record sheet which is kept or carried for the purposes of complying with the EC regulations which the person knows is false, or he has altered a record or entry, or has caused the alteration of a record or entry with intent to deceive, then the authorised examiner may seize the record.

Receipts for Seized Charts
Normally the enforcement officer will provide a receipt for any seized charts. This is normally done on the next chart which the driver will use to continue making records after the seizure of the chart or charts.

Return of Seized Charts
If there is no charge within six months of the seizure of charts and they have not been returned to the person from whom they were taken then a Magistrates' Court can order the disposal of the charts and award costs if necessary depending on the circumstances. Requests to the court for such an order may be made by the person from whom the charts were taken or by an enforcement officer.

Charts in Legal Proceedings

Tachograph charts produced on recording equipment installed in vehicles in accordance with the regulations are evidence of the matters appearing from the record in the case of any proceedings under Part VI of the Transport Act 1968. In other words any actual recording made by the instrument or any entry made on a chart by a driver is taken as direct evidence, admissible in court, that what is shown is true fact. Thus if there are any breaches of the drivers' hours law or record-keeping regulations the evidence from the chart will satisfy the court on the matter.

Speeding

In other instances charts may or may not be used as evidence depending on the circumstances. Where the driver has exceeded speed limits it has been clearly established that the chart evidence alone cannot be used to bring a prosecution for speeding. In order to do this the police must produce additional witness or corroborative evidence of their own (from radar, vascar or other devices or by conventional pacing methods). However, the driver does have a right to use the evidence on the chart to defend himself against a charge of speeding if he genuinely believes he has been wrongly accused. In order to do this he must get the chart signed at the time he was stopped to prove later that this was the chart he was using at the relevant time and he must get the chart properly analysed and the kph speed recording accurately converted to mph in order to present his defence.

There are other circumstances related to speeding where the evidence of a chart may be used against a driver in respect of other driving charges. For example, if a vehicle was observed to be travelling at speed through a dangerous, narrow or crowded street and the vehicle registration number was reported to the police and witness statements were given, then when the vehicle is traced and the driver's chart examined it could be produced as evidence in a charge of driving without due consideration, without due care, or even careless or reckless driving. Conversely, the chart may have shown the vehicle speed to be quite reasonable and within the limits and therefore no such charge could be justified. Licensing Authorities will accept evidence of speeding from charts for the purposes of penalising heavy vehicle drivers and their Heavy Goods Vehicle driving licences can and will be suspended in such cases.

Accidents

Similar situations apply in respect of vehicle accidents which are discussed in detail in the main text. For the purposes of the point being made, a chart may be taken following an accident and the evidence of vehicle speed both before and at the moment of the accident may be used to justify driving charges against the driver if he was at fault in driving too fast for the conditions. On the other hand, the chart may show that his driving was not unreasonable in the circumstances and, despite what an hysterical witness vouched about his speed, there would be no justification in bringing driving charges against him.

Already there have been many reported cases in Britain where drivers have been saved from serious driving charges or from any charges at all based on the evidence of their tachograph charts.

It must be pointed out that in the case of accidents, police do have powers to seize any tachograph chart in a vehicle for the purposes of forensic examination of evidence.

NOTES:

The following notes on points of interpretation may be helpful in relation to the text in this chapter.

1. Reasonable Excuse:

    The regulations do not specify the type of 'reasonable excuse' which the courts may accept in the case of loss of a chart. However, it seems likely where the loss occurred as a result of an accident or incident over which the driver had no control or in the case of theft or vandalism of a vehicle containing a chart or charts these may be considered reasonable excuses because the facts of the accident or incident could be established. Also where drivers are on extended international journeys or are delayed by circumstances outside their control from returning from international journeys these would appear to constitute reasonable excuses. On the other hand, petty excuses about charts left in overalls, in other vehicles, at home where children destroyed them and other frivolous excuses would less likely be accepted.

2. First Employer:

    This point leaves open to doubt the correct interpretation of 'first' employer. It could be construed to be the driver's main 'or full-time' employer which would be the most logical and sensible practical interpretation. However, if the literal interpretation of the 'first' is applied then a situation could arise where a driver has two employers and he has worked longer for the part-time employer that charts produced in the employ of the main or full-time employer would have to be returned to the part-time employer.

15: Tachograph-Related Vehicle Equipment – New Technology Developments

The tachograph as we have known it in the past and certainly since its mandatory introduction in Britain in 1980 is, by modern technology standards, almost antiquated in concept. The need for drivers to handle, write on and generally look after small, circular pieces of damage-sensitive paper is 'old hat' in the current hi-tec environment. However, this situation has its advantages as well as disadvantages. For the owner-driver haulier and small lorry or coach fleet operator the instrument provides a robust and relatively simple means of complying with legal record-keeping requirements. For larger fleet operators, while interest is increasing in the latest in-cab computers with facilities for direct down-loading of data into the office computer and in other on-board monitoring equipment, the fact is that the law still requires the use of the tachograph as we know it and as covered in this book. It is likely to be many years yet before basic tachograph-concept statutory requirements encapsulated in EC law will be changed so radically as to allow the collection, transmission and storage of important legislatively-controlled data, such as drivers' working, driving rest and break period times, by 'unseen' means. So we have to live with the tachograph for some time to come.

Having said this, it is useful for the vehicle operator, whether owner-driver, small or large fleet owner to have an inkling of both the availability of tachograph-related, on-board monitoring equipment such as fuel consumption meters and the developing technology of in-cab computers. His interest may be only to keep up with what is happening in the industry but he may see this as a step towards 'preparing the way' for the introduction of modern facilities into his own fleet operation. For this reason, an outline of such equipment and developments has been included here. There is, however, some difficulty in doing so because of the very rapid rate of developments. The new technology of today will be outmoded, even antiquated, in next to no time. So too will the next generation of equipment and the one after that. We have seen this with hi-fi; we have seen it with cameras and we have especially seen it with microcomputers. Exactly the same is happening with on-board or in-cab vehicle equipment.

There is now an enormous demand in transport for monitoring, recording and communications facilities so that while the vehicle may be physically away from base the driver remains in contact and the operator knows broadly what happens to his vehicle during that time. Gone are the days when the vehicle disappeared out of the gate in the morning to be out of sight and out of mind until it returned, hopefully, at the end of the day with load delivered, hopefully again, to the right place. Nowadays, the capital investment involved and the operating costs incurred in vehicle operations plus the competition and pressures of business demand much more sophistication in controls and communication. Hence the initial development and continuous improvements in equipment such as that described in the following text.

Fuel Monitoring

With vehicle fuel constituting a major cost factor in transport operating budgets there is concern to improve the efficiency of its use and reduce wastage. With the aid of a vehicle-mounted fuel consumption measuring system the operator can determine quite accurately the amount of fuel used by a vehicle over an extended period of time but also on a daily basis if required or even for a particular individual journey. Additionally, the monitoring of fuel consumption can draw the operator's attention to bad driving habits such as unnecessary speeding and generally erratic driving and costly vehicle defects and maladjustments such as excessive idling speeds and binding brakes. It further enables an analysis of routes on a fuel-consumed basis thus enabling the operator to re-route or re-schedule to avoid regularly congested areas and peak-time or seasonal traffic hold-ups.

The Lucas Kienzle system (which is a leader in this field) comprises a meter based on single chamber measuring with the use of elliptical gears to achieve inherently accurate and reliable fuel measurement together with a fuel counter or an in-cab digital display. The equipment is claimed to be accurate to within plus or minus two per cent and permits a maximum throughput of up to 120 litres per hour. The in-cab display has a 6-digit non-adjustable (ie it cannot be zeroed) accumulating counter that continuously indicates the cumulative consumption of the vehicle (in litres and tenths of litres) from the time the system was first installed and commissioned. It provides the driver with details of his actual running fuel consumption, the average consumption for the trip, the total consumption for the trip and the distance covered either totally or on a trip.

In conjunction with, or as an alternative to, the in-cab display, it is possible to link the meter to the tachograph by means of the fourth stylus (see p 50). This enables fuel consumption to be recorded directly on to the automatic-type tachograph chart where it can be assessed against the speed and distance recordings. The recording on the chart indicates every time two litres of fuel (and then ten litres) have passed through the meter and been consumed by the engine. There are also facilities for the fuel consumption recording to be downloaded for processing by the Lucas Kienzle M-FOS micro-computer system.

The fuel consumption meter can be fitted permanently to vehicles or can be obtained as a rapid-fit system to enable it to be used with quick release connections for switching from one vehicle to another and then another.

Road Speed Limiters

Fuel economy, as we have already seen, is a major cost consideration for transport fleet operators and for this reason there is demand for equipment which helps to reduce this cost. Restricting the top speed of vehicles is an important and signifi-

Figure 15.1   *Lucas Kienzle fuel consumption display unit mounted in cab*

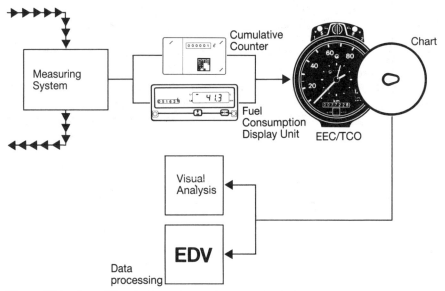

Figure 15.2   *Lucas Kienzle electronic metering system for fuel consumption*

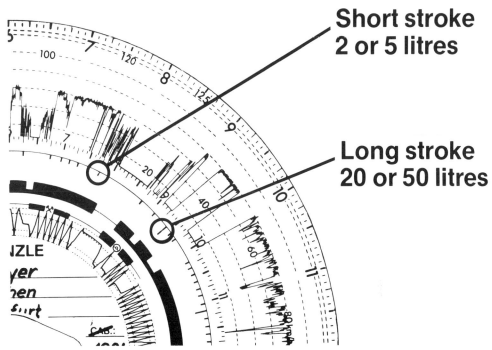

Figure 15.3   *Lucas Kienzle automatic tachograph chart with additional stylus trace for indicating fuel consumption*

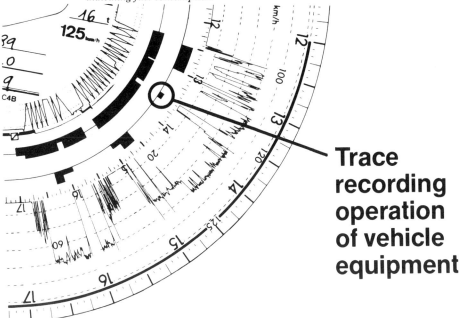

Figure 15.4   *Lucas Kienzle automatic tachograph chart with additional stylus trace indicating the use of on-board vehicle equipment*

cant method of reducing fuel consumption costs and this can be achieved by the fitment of a road speed limiter. Restricting speed in this way provides a number of benefits. First, it reduces fuel consumption by keeping road speeds to within acceptable and predetermined limits; second, it enables the cost saving benefits of other economy aids such as air deflectors to be realised; third, it helps to reduce wear and tear on the vehicle engine, transmission, running gear brakes and tyres and, overall, it reduces maintenance costs; fourth, it reduces the risk of accident and thus, in the long term, it has beneficial effects on insurance premiums and it reduces the stress on the driver.

Road speed limiters normally include three major components, a road speed sensor, a control module and an actuator. The speed sensor is normally installed in the tachograph or speedometer driveline and this sends a signal to the control module. When the road speed reaches a pre-set limit, the module activates the actuator which in turn controls the fuel pump lever to reduce the amount of fuel injected into the engine. This effectively reduces the road speed of the vehicle. When this has been achieved, the control module senses the change in speed and stops or reverses the actuator so that fuel continues to flow into the engine. Thus the system is designed to regulate fuel flow in cycles to regulate the road speed of the vehicle within the pre-set limit irrespective of the fact that the driver may have his accelerator foot hard to the floor.

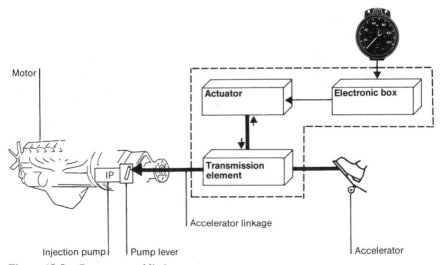

Figure 15.5 *Compact speed limiter system*

The secret of an effective speed limiter is that it must not affect the driveability of the vehicle to the point where the driver feels the engine 'hunting' or that he has lost power. This problem is overcome on the Lucas Kienzle system by the use of electronic control and an electric actuator. Such is the speed and sensitivity of the control that it can sense vehicle acceleration as well as road speed, and it can sense inclines so the control module automatically 'instructs' the actuator to increase the fuel throughput to compensate. Vehicles fitted with the latest Lucas Kienzle 1318 and 1314 series tachographs have the advantage that speed signals, produced by the same sensors used in the instruments, can be directly connected from the rear of the tachograph head (where there is a 'road speed' terminal) to the electronic control module.

Where a vehicle is fitted with a road speed limiter of this type, the driver retains absolute control over the vehicle by use of the accelerator and he has full power in the intermediate gears up to the point of the pre-set maximum road speed. The limiter comes into operation progressively as the top speed is reached to give the driver warning that it is coming into effect. He does not experience a sudden, so-called 'loss' of power.

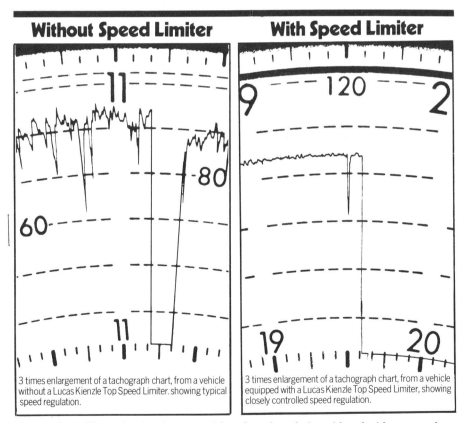

Figure 15.6 *Illustration showing comparision of speed regulation with and without a speed limiter*

For urban delivery operations, an additional facility can be incorporated in the control module to limit maximum engine revolutions in each gear as well as maximum road speed. The system will respond to whichever limit is reached first and will therefore provide operational cost savings on vehicles which may have spent little or no time at all on roads where maximum speeds can be achieved.

Legal Requirements

The law in the UK★ requires the fitment of speed limiters (complying with BSAu 217, Part 1 1987) to coaches first used from 1 April 1974 if they are capable of a maximum speed in excess of 70mph. The actual date from which a speed limiter must be fitted depends on the date of first use of the vehicle as follows:

First used	Date for fitment
1 April 1974 – 31 March 1984	1 April 1991
1 April 1984 – 31 March 1989	1 April 1990
After 1 April 1989	From date of first use

★ *The Road Vehicles (Construction and Use) Regulations 1986 as amended.*

Currently there is no requirement for the fitment of these devices on heavy goods vehicles although the idea has been mooted by the Department of Transport following a number of serious heavy vehicle speed-related accidents. The transport trade associations are promoting the idea, and the industry itself is anxious, that improvements in driver behaviour in this respect should be induced by voluntary rather than compulsory means.

In-cab Computers

By the standards of modern-day technological development, tachographs as we know them are 'old hat'. However, as has been made clear in this book, the law still demands their use in a very large number of over 3.5 tonne maximum permissible weight goods vehicles throughout Europe and in many passenger vehicles too. This has not stopped either the development of, or the demand by, many operators for more sophisticated reporting, monitoring and data collection devices in their vehicles (basically, in-cab computers), or indeed for other methods of communication which are, in any case, outside the context of this book. Here we can look just briefly at development trends in this field to indicate to the reader what , in outline, the future may hold. Other books more specifically devoted to the new technology can be studied for detailed explanations of the technical specifications and the operational uses for such equipment.

The result of this demand and development is the emergence of the in-cab or on-board (choose whichever term you prefer) computer. We are led to believe that there are at least some 80,000 to 100,000 users of such equipment in the USA but clearly this must be a moving figure with the possibility of fleet operators adding to the statistics day by day. But it is interesting to note the trend because we, in the UK and in Europe, invariably follow what happens on the other side of the Atlantic ocean.

Broadly, the development of such equipment has been along two routes. By the vehicle manufacturers on the one hand who have specific interests in being able to store and transmit data relating to the vehicle's mechanical condition (such as with the BMW motor car in-built system) and who provide their user customers with data relevant to their own business needs, and by ancillary equipment manufacturers whose interests follow more the demand from customers such as those in the transport and distribution industries who need to collect and analyse operational data about vehicle activities, about driver performance and about the logistics of delivery services.

MAN System

An example of vehicle manufacturer-oriented systems is that developed by MAN the West German heavy truck maker. This system involves the use of an on-board computer to record data about both the trip and the vehicle via a series of sensors. During the trip the driver has a portable hand-computer connected to the on-board computer which he uses to input data about his delivery schedule given to him prior to the journey and about such matters as refuelling of the vehicle. On return to base the hand-computer is taken into the office and located on to a data reading station. Here it will transfer all the vehicle-produced data and the driver input data to the main computer for processing, analysis and storage.

The hand-computer is battery driven and is programmable. It has a 38-key keyboard and a 7-line LCD display. In the vehicle the unit sits in a special holder which acts as both an interface for the vehicle computer and as a charging unit. The actual vehicle computer itself is a data acquisition unit with a non-volatile semi-conductor memory. It has 16 analog inputs and 24 digital in/outputs.

Principally, the system provides for the input of trip data such as details of all deliveries and consignments. During the trip vehicle moving and standing times are recorded, distances between stops and fuel consumption. The route or schedule for the trip can be called up on the display to show the next customer address, appointed delivery time and other relevant information. At the delivery point the driver can input details of the actual delivery made, any shortages, damages, returns, empties and even the customer's next order. The time spent at the stop is recorded. Subsequently, any change of driver, or of trailer as well as refuelling details can be input. On return to base, all the driver has to do is hand in his portable computer unit for that day's data to be cleared via the desk-top microcomputer and for the next day's delivery schedule data to be input.

Lucas Kienzle System

Lucas Kienzle is a good example of the ancillary equipment manufacture developing new technology equipment for the transport industry and it too markets its own in-cab computer. This unit can receive information, via an optical port, from the latest 1318 series tachograph instrument. The data can be stored electronically for subsequent downloading to the depot based computer. Infra-red transmission is used to reduce the need for reading tachograph chart data manually for legislative needs. As soon as the data link has been established, the base computer acquires all information from the vehicle that is needed to update its records. This information can be analysed using software specially developed by Lucas Kienzle

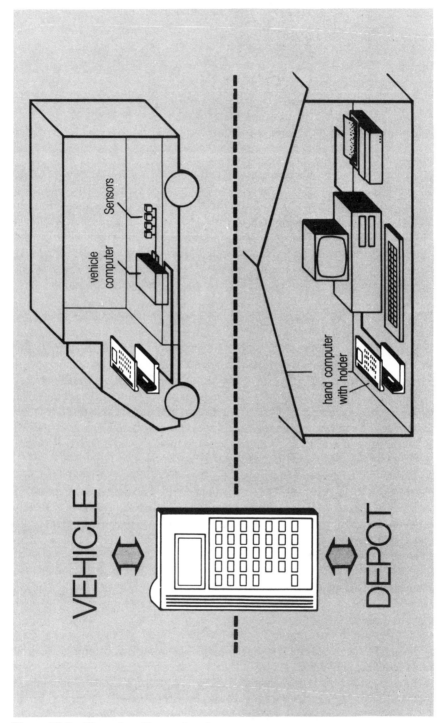

Figure 15.7   *Illustration of how an in-cab computer system operates*

in conjunction with the UK Department of Transport. Additional information can be transmitted to assist in improving fleet efficiency through the rapid analysis of data.

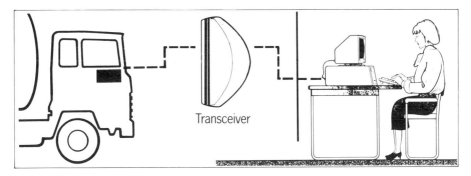

Figure 15.8 *Illustration of Lucas Kienzle in-cab computer system*

The Kienzle model 1318 instrument is claimed to be the most advanced tachograph yet made, possessing the facility to transmit information via its optical port as described above to either a vehicle mounted or an in-cab computer. This particular tachograph can be fitted with the fuel consumption meter referred to earlier in this chapter and thus is able to transmit fuel consumption data through its output port.

The Lucas Kienzle in-cab computer incorporates a display that can be used to convey numerical information to the driver, in particular, time driven and accumulated rest time with a facility to warn when the next break period is due. Certain aspects of vehicle or load condition can be linked to display or make audible warning of conditions needing the driver's attention (increased temperature in a refrigerated vehicle for example). A facility exists for the driver to be alerted by means of an LED as to the most economical operating condition for the vehicle in terms of engine revolutions. This helps to achieve improved fuel economy.

The Future
The systems described in outline above are just two examples of a number of such systems available and many more are in the process of development. It is likely that the next few years will see a proliferation of this type of equipment even to the point where it may become standard fitment on some heavy vehicles. Clearly, there are operational benefits to be achieved from its use but there are also capital and operating costs to be justified. For large fleet operators this must surely be the way forward in fleet management. For the owner-driver haulier and small fleet owner the future may remain with the basic tachograph but, as this book has shown, this instrument can be put to very effective use in providing useful operational data that will help improve the efficiency, the productivity and the economy of vehicle operations.

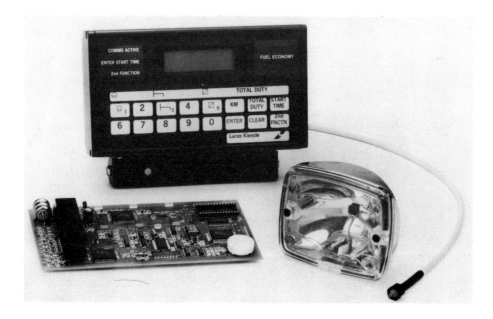

Figure 15.9   *Components of Lucas Kienzle in-cab computer system*

Other Equipment

It would be remiss to conclude this book without mentioning two further items of tachograph-related equipment.

Tach-Trak

This is a pocket calculator sized instrument which simulates the information being recorded by the tachograph instrument and makes it instantly available to the driver. Its key feature is that it helps drivers determine how many hours they have driven and how much more time they can spend driving before legal limits are reached. It also logs and counts the accumulation of break periods and gives advance warning of infringements. The instrument is light and portable, easy to use and a boon to the driver who may find the problems of trying to calculate relevant times direct from his tachograph chart just too difficult. It reduces the risk of law breaking and, some users claim, it helps the driver to utilise more fully what limited driving time he does have available without actually overstepping the limit.

ICS Black Box

This is a piece of equipment which is claimed to perform a similar function to the tachograph but is capable of 'reading' sixty days' information. The instrument is slightly smaller than a video cassette and is identified to an individual vehicle with a removable module. It records date, time, speed, distance, odometer readings and engine running times. It will also accept two separate monitor functions (eg PTO operation or tailgate opening). The instrument has a capability to store 8 kilobytes of information at one time and downloads data to a base computer (a desk-top personal computer). This unit can be linked to a tachograph mode switch to allow recording of driver activities which can then be analysed via suitable software. More sophisticated versions of the basic Black Box have a keyboard and crystal display and can store very detailed information on a host of delivery-related activities as well as fuel monitoring.

Appendices

I Tachograph Legislation (EC 3821/85)
II Exemptions from Tachograph Fitment and Use (UK Derogations)
III Summary of EC Drivers' Hours Law (EC 3820/85)
IV Bibliography of Relevant UK Legislation
V Tachographs and UK Annual Vehicle Testing
VI Approved Tachograph Centres in the UK
VII Useful Addresses

Appendix I

Tachograph Legislation (EC 3821/85)

COUNCIL REGULATION (EEC) No 3821/85
of 20 December 1985
on recording equipment in road transport

THE COUNCIL OF THE EUROPEAN COMMUNITIES,

Having regard to the Treaty establishing the European Economic Community, and in particular Article 75 thereof,

Having regard to the proposal from the Commission,

Having regard to the opinion of the European Parliament,

Having regard to the opinion of the Economic and Social Committee,

Whereas Regulation (EEC) No 1463/70 as last amended by Regulation (EEC) No 2828/77 introduced recording equipment in road transport;

Whereas, taking into account the amendments set out hereinafter, in order to clarify matters, all the relevant provisions should be brought together in a single text, and in consequence thereof, Regulation (EEC) No 1463/70 of the Council should be repealed; whereas, however, certain passenger services should be maintained in force for a certain time;

Whereas the use of recording equipment that may indicate the periods of time referred to in Regulation (EEC) No 3820/85 on the harmonization of certain social legislation relating to road transport is intended to ensure effective checking on that social legislation;

Whereas the obligation to use such recording equipment can be imposed only for vehicles registered in Member States; whereas furthermore certain of such vehicles may, without giving rise to difficulty, be excluded from the scope of this Regulation;

Whereas the Member States should be entitled, with the Commission's authorization, to grant certain vehicles exemptions from the provisions of the Regulation in exceptional circumstances; whereas, in urgent cases, it should be possible to grant these exemptions for a limited time without prior authorization from the Commission;

Whereas in order to ensure effective checking, the equipment must be reliable in operation, easy to use and designed in such a way as to minimize any possibility of fraudulent use; whereas to this end recording equipment should in particular be capable of providing on separate sheets for each driver and in a sufficiently precise and easily readable form, recorded details of the various periods of time;

Whereas automatic recording of other details of a vehicle's journey, such as speed and distance covered will contribute significantly to road safety and will encourage sensible driving of the vehicle; whereas, consequently, it appears appropriate to provide for the equipment also to record those details;

Whereas it is necessary to set Community construction and installation standards for recording equipment and to provide for an EEC approval procedure, in order to avoid throughout the territory of the Member States any impediment to the registration of vehicles fitted with such recording equipment, to their entry into service or use, or to such equipment being used;

Whereas, in the event of differences of opinion between Member States concerning cases of EEC type approval, the Commission should be empowered to take a decision on a dispute within six months if the States concerned have been unable to reach a settlement;

Whereas it would be helpful in implementing this Regulation and preventing abuses to issue drivers who so request with a copy of their record sheets;

Whereas, in order to achieve the aims hereinbefore mentioned of keeping a check on work and rest periods it is necessary that employers and drivers be responsible for seeing that the equipment functions correctly and that they perform with due care the operations prescribed;

Whereas the provisions governing the number of record sheets that a driver must keep with him must be amended following the replacement of the flexible week by a fixed week;

Whereas technical progress necessitates rapid adaptation of the technical specifications set out in the Annexes to this Regulation; whereas, in order to facilitate the implementation of the measures necessary for this purpose, provision should be made for a procedure establishing close cooperation between the Member States and the Commission within an Advisory Committee;

Whereas Member States should exchange the available information on breaches established;

Whereas in order to ensure that recording equipment functions reliably and correctly, it is advisable to lay down uniform requirements for the periodic checks and inspections to which the equipment is to be subject after installation,

HAS ADOPTED THIS REGULATION:

CHAPTER I
Principles and scope

Article 1

Recording equipment within the meaning of this Regulation shall, as regards construction, installation, use and testing, comply with the requirements of this Regulation and of Annexes I and II thereto, which shall form an integral part of this Regulation.

Article 2

For the purpose of this Regulation the definitions set out in Article 1 of Regulation (EEC) No 3820/85 shall apply.

Article 3

1. Recording equipment shall be installed and used in vehicles registered in a Member State which are used for the carriage of passengers or goods by road, except the vehicles referred to in Article 4 and 14 (1) of Regulation (EEC) No 3820/85.

2. Member States may exempt vehicles mentioned in Article 13 (1) of Regulation (EEC) No 3820/85 from application of this Regulation. Member States shall inform the Commission of any exemption granted under this paragraph.

3. Member States may, after authorization by the Commission, exempt from application of this Regulation vehicles used for the transport operations referred to in Article 13(2) of Regulation (EEC) No 3820/85. In urgent cases they may grant a temporary exemption for a period not exceeding 30 days, which shall be notified immediately to the Commission. The Commission shall notify the other Member States of any exemption granted pursuant to this paragraph.

4. In the case of national transport operations, Member States may require the installation and use of recording equipment in accordance with this Regulation in any of the vehicles for which its installation and use are not required by paragraph 1

CHAPTER II
Type approval

Article 4
Applications for EEC approval of a type of recording equipment or of a model record sheet shall be submitted, accompanied by the appropriate specifications, by the manufacturer or his agent to a Member State. No application in respect of any one type of recording equipment or of any one model record sheet may be submitted to more than one Member State.

Article 5
A Member State shall grant EEC approval to any type of recording equipment or to any model record sheet which conforms to the requirements laid down in Annex I to this Regulation, provided the Member State is in a position to check that production models conform to the approved prototype.

Any modifications or additions to an approved model must receive additional EEC type approval from the Member State which granted the original EEC type approval.

Article 6
Member States shall issue to the applicant an EEC approval mark, which shall conform to the model shown in Annex II, for each type of recording equipment or model record sheet which they approve pursuant to Article 5.

Article 7
The competent authorities of the Member State to which the application for type approval has been submitted shall, in respect of each type of recording equipment or model record sheet which they approve or refuse to approve, either send within one month to the authorities of the other Member States a copy of the approval certificate accompanied by copies of the relevant specifications or, if such is the case, notify those authorities that approval has been refused; in cases of refusal they shall communicate the reasons for their decision.

Article 8
1. If a Member State which has granted EEC type approval as provided for in Article 5 finds that certain recording equipment or record sheets bearing the EEC type approval mark which it has issued do not conform to the prototype which it has approved, it shall take the necessary measures to ensure that production models conform to the approved prototype. The measures taken may, if necessary, extend to withdrawal of EEC type approval.
2. A Member State which has granted EEC type approval shall withdraw such approval if the recording equipment or record sheet which has been approved is not in conformity with this Regulation or its Annexes or displays in use any general defect which makes it unsuitable for the purpose for which it is intended.
3. If a Member State which has granted EEC type approval is notified by another Member State of one of the cases referred to in paragraphs 1 and 2, it shall also, after consulting the latter Member State, take the steps laid down in those paragraphs, subject to paragraph 5.
4. A Member State which ascertains that one of the cases referred to in paragraph 2 has arisen may forbid until further notice the placing on the market and putting into service of the recording equipment or record sheets. The same applies in the cases mentioned in paragraph 1 with respect to recording equipment or record sheets which have been exempted

from EEC initial verification, if the manufacturer, after due warning, does not bring the equipment into line with the approved model or with the requirements of this Regulation.

In any event the competent authorities of the Member States shall notify one another and the Commission, within one month, of any withdrawal of EEC type approval or of any other measures taken pursuant to paragraphs 1, 2 and 3 and shall specify the reasons for such action.

5. If a Member State which has granted an EEC type approval disputes the existence of any of the cases specified in paragraphs 1 or 2 notified to it, the Member States concerned shall endeavour to settle the dispute and the Commission shall be kept informed.

If talks between the Member States have not resulted in agreement within four months of the date of the notification referred to in paragraph 3 above, the Commission, after consulting experts from all Member States and having considered all the relevant factors, e.g. economic and technical factors, shall within six months adopt a decision which shall be communicated to the Member States concerned and at the same time to the other Member States. The Commission shall lay down in each instance the time limit for implementation of its decision.

Article 9

1. An applicant for EEC type approval of a model record sheet shall state on his application the type or types of recording equipment on which the sheet in question is designed to be used and shall provide suitable equipment of such type or types for the purpose of testing the sheet.

2. The competent authorities of each Member State shall indicate on the approval certificate for the model record sheet the type or types of recording equipment on which that model sheet may be used.

Article 10

No Member State may refuse to register any vehicle fitted with recording equipment, or prohibit the entry into service or use of such vehicle for any reason connected with the fact that the vehicle is fitted with such equipment, if the equipment bears the EEC approval mark referred to in Article 6 and the installation plaque referred to in Article 12.

Article 11

All decisions pursuant to this Regulation refusing or withdrawing approval of a type of recording equipment or model record sheet shall specify in detail the reasons on which they are based. A decision shall be communicated to the party concerned, who shall at the same time be informed of the remedies available to him under the laws of the Member States and of the time-limits for the exercise of such remedies.

CHAPTER III
Installation and inspection

Article 12

1. Recording equipment may be installed or repaired only by fitters or workshops approved by the competent authorities of Member States for that purpose after the latter, should they so desire, have heard the views of the manufacturers concerned.

2. The approved fitter or workshop shall place a special mark on the seals which it affixes. The competent authorities of each Member State shall maintain a register of the marks used.

3. The competent authorities of the Member States shall send each other their lists of approved fitters or workshops and also copies of the marks used.

4. For the purpose of certifying that installation of recording equipment took place in

accordance with the requirements of this Regulation an installation plaque affixed as provided in Annex I shall be used.

CHAPTER IV
Use of equipment

Article 13

The employer and drivers shall be responsible for seeing that the equipment functions correctly.

Article 14

1. The employer shall issue a sufficient number of record sheets to drivers, bearing in mind the fact that these sheets are personal in character, the length of the period of service and the possible obligation to replace sheets which are damaged, or have been taken by an authorised inspecting officer. The employer shall issue to drivers only sheets of an approved model suitable for use in the equipment installed in the vehicle.
2. The undertaking shall keep the record sheets in good order for at least a year after their use and shall give copies to the drivers concerned who request them. The sheets shall be produced or handed over at the request of any authorized inspecting officer.

Article 15

1. Drivers shall not use dirty or damaged record sheets. The sheets shall be adequately protected on this account.
2. Drivers shall use the record sheets every day on which they are driving, starting from the moment they take over the vehicle. The record sheet shall not be withdrawn before the end of the daily working period unless its withdrawal is otherwise authorized. No record sheet may be used to cover a period longer than that for which it is intended.

When, as a result of being away from the vehicle, a driver is unable to use the equipment fitted to the vehicle, the periods of time indicated in paragraph 3, second indent (b), (c) and (d) below shall be entered on the sheet, either manually, by automatic recording or other means, legibly and without dirtying the sheet.

Drivers shall amend the record sheets as necessary should there be more than one driver on board the vehicle, so that the information referred to in Chapter II (1) to (3) of Annex I is recorded on the record sheet of the driver who is actually driving.
3. Drivers shall:

– ensure that the time recorded on the sheet agrees with the official time in the country of registration of the vehicle,
– operate the switch mechanisms enabling the following periods of time to be recorded separately and distinctly:
    (a) under the sign : driving time;
    (b) under the sign : all other periods of work;
    (c) under the sign : other periods of availability,
       namely:
       – waiting time, i.e. the period during which drivers need remain at their posts only for the purpose of answering any calls to start or resume driving or to carry out other work,
       – time spent beside the driver while the vehicle is in motion,
       – time spent on a bunk while the vehicle is in motion;
    (d) under the sign : breaks in work and daily rest periods.

4. Each Member State may permit all the periods referred to in paragraph 3, second indent (b) and (c) to be recorded under the sign .... on the record sheets used on vehicles registered in its territory.

5. Each crew member shall enter the following information on his record sheet;

(a) on beginning to use the sheet – his surname and first name;

(b) the date and place where use of the sheet begins and the date and place where such use ends;

(c) the registration number of each vehicle to which he is assigned, both at the start of the first journey recorded on the sheet and then, in the event of a change of vehicle, during use of the sheet;

(d) the odometer reading:
  – at the start of the first journey recorded on the sheet,
  – at the end of the last journey recorded on the sheet,
  – in the event of a change of vehicle during a working day (reading on the vehicle to which he was assigned and reading on the vehicle to which he is to be assigned);

(e) the time of any change of vehicle.

6. The equipment shall be so designed that it is possible for an authorized inspecting officer, if necessary after opening the equipment, to read the recordings relating to the nine hours preceding the time of the check without permanently deforming, damaging or soiling the sheet.

The equipment shall, furthermore, be so designed that it is possible without opening the case, to verify that recordings are being made.

7. Whenever requested by an authorized inspecting officer to do so, the driver must be able to produce record sheets for the current week, and in any case for the last day of the previous week on which he drove.

Article 16

1. In the event of breakdown or faulty operation of the equipment, the employer shall have it repaired by an approved fitter or workshop, as soon as circumstances permit.

If the vehicle is unable to return to the premises within a period of one week calculated from the day of the breakdown or of the discovery of defective operation, the repair shall be carried out *en route*.

Measures taken by Member States pursuant to Article 19 may give the competent authorities power to prohibit the use of the vehicle in cases where breakdown or faulty operation has not been put right as provided in the foregoing subparagraphs.

2. While the equipment is unserviceable or operating defectively, drivers shall mark on the record sheet or sheets, or on a temporary sheet to be attached to the record sheet, all information for the various periods of time which is not recorded correctly by the equipment.

CHAPTER V
Final provisions

Article 17

The amendments necessary to adapt the Annexes to technical progress shall be adopted in accordance with the procedure laid down in Article 18

Article 18

1. A Committee for the adaption of this Regulation to technical progress (hereinafter called 'the Committee') is hereby set up; it shall consist of representatives of the Member States, and a representative of the Commission shall be chairman.

2. The Committee shall adopt its own rules of procedure.

3. Where the procedure laid down in this Article is to be followed, the matter shall be

referred to the Committee by the chairman, either on his own initiative or at the request of the representative of a Member State.

4. The Commission representative shall submit to the Committee a draft of the measures to be taken. The Committee shall give its opinion on that draft within a time limit set by the chairman having regard to the urgency of the matter. Opinions shall be delivered by a qualified majority in accordance with Article 148 (2) of the Treaty. The chairman shall not vote.

5. (a) The Commission shall adopt the envisaged measures where they are in accordance with the opinion of the Committee.

   (b) Where the measures envisaged are not in accordance with the opinion of the Committee or if no opinion is delivered, the Commission shall without delay submit to the Council a proposal on the measures to be taken. The Council shall act by a qualified majority.

   (c) If the Council has not acted within three months of the proposal being submitted to it, the proposed measures shall be adopted by the Commission.

Article 19

1. Member States shall, in good time and after consulting the Commission, adopt such laws, regulations or administrative provisions as may be necessary for the implementation of this Regulation.

Such measures shall cover, *inter alia*, the reorganization of, procedure for, and means of carrying out, checks on compliance and the penalties to be imposed in case of breach.

2. Member States shall assist each other in applying this Regulation and in checking compliance therewith.

3. Within this framework of this mutual assistance the competent authorities of the Member States shall regularly send one another all available information concerning:

– breaches of this Regulation committed by non-residents and any penalties imposed for such breaches,
– penalties imposed by a Member State on its residents for such breaches committed in other Member States.

Article 20

Regulation (EEC) No 1463/70 shall be repealed.

However, Article 3 (1) of the said Regulation shall, until 31 December 1989, continue to apply to vehicles and drivers employed in regular international passenger services in so far as the vehicles used for such services are not fitted with recording equipment used as prescribed in this Regulation.

Article 21

This Regulation shall enter into force on 29 September 1986.

This Regulation shall be binding in its entirety and directly applicable in all Member States.

Done at Brussels, 20 December 1985.

For the Council
The President
R. KRIEPS

ANNEX I

REQUIREMENTS FOR CONSTRUCTION, TESTING, INSTALLATION AND INSPECTION

I DEFINITIONS

In this Annex:

(a) **Recording equipment means:**

equipment intended for installation in road vehicles to show and record automatically or semi-automatically details of the movement of those vehicles and of certain working periods of their drivers;

(b) **Record sheet means:**

a sheet designed to accept and retain recorded data, to be placed in the recording equipment and on which the marking devices of the latter inscribe a continuous record of the information to be recorded;

(c) **The constant of the recording equipment means:**

the numerical characteristic giving the value of the input signal required to show and record a distance travelled of one kilometre; this constant must be expressed either in revolutions per kilometre (k ...rev/km), or in impulses per kilometre (k ...imp/km).

(d) **Characteristic coefficient of the means:**

the numerical characteristic giving the value of the output signal emitted by the part of the vehicle linking it with the recording equipment (gearbox output shaft or axle) while the vehicle travels a distance of one measured kilometre under normal test conditions (see Chapter VI point 4 of this Annex). The characteristic coefficient is expressed either in revolutions per kilometre (w = ... rev/km) or in impulses per kilometre (w = ...imp/km).

(e) **Effective circumference of wheel tyres means:**

the average of the distances travelled by the several wheels moving the vehicle (driving wheels) in the course of the complete rotation. The measurement of these distances must be made under normal test conditions (see Chapter V1 point 4 of this Annex) and is expressed on the form: 1 = ...mm.

II GENERAL CHARACTERISTICS AND FUNCTIONS OF RECORDING EQUIPMENT

The equipment must be able to record the following:

1. distance travelled by the vehicle;
2. speed of the vehicle;
3. driving time;
4. other periods of work or of availability;
5. breaks from work and daily rest periods;
6. opening of the case containing the record sheet;

For vehicles used by two drivers the equipment must be capable of recording simultaneously but distinctly and on two separate sheets details of the periods listed under 3, 4 and 5.

III CONSTRUCTION REQUIREMENTS FOR RECORDING EQUIPMENT

(a) **General points**

1. *Recording equipment shall include the following;*

1.1. Visual instruments showing
  – distance travelled (distance recorder),
  – speed (speedometer),
  – time (clock).

1.2. Recording instruments comprising;
  – a recorder of the distance travelled,
  – a speed recorder,
  – one or more time recorders satisfying the requirements laid down in Chapter III(c) 4.

1.3. A marking device showing on the record sheet each opening of the case containing that sheet.

2. Any inclusion in the equipment of devices additional to those listed above must not interfere with the proper operation of the mandatory devices or with the reading of them.

   The equipment must be submitted for approval complete with any such additional devices.

3. *Materials*

3.1. All the constituent parts of the recording equipment must be made of materials with sufficient stability and mechanical strength and stable electrical and magnetic characteristics.

3.2. Any modification in a constituent part of the equipment or in the nature of the materials used for its manufacture must, before being applied in manufacture, be submitted for approval to the authority which granted type-approval for the equipment.

4. *Measurement of distance travelled*

   The distances travelled may be measured and recorded either;
   – so as to include both forward and reverse movement, or
   – so as to include only forward movement
   Any recordings of reversing movements must on no account affect the clarity and accuracy of the other recordings.

5. *Measurement of speed*

5.1. The range of speed measurement shall be as stated in the type approval certificate.

5.2. The natural frequency and the damping of the measuring device must be such that the instruments showing and recording the speed can, within the range of measurement, follow acceleration changes of up to 2 m/s2 within the limits of accepted tolerances.

6. *Measurement of time (clock)*

6.1. The control of the mechanism for resetting the clock must be located inside a case containing the record sheet; each opening of that case must be automatically recorded on the record sheet.

6.2. If the forward movement mechanism of the record sheet is controlled by the clock the period during which the latter will run correctly after being fully wound must be greater by at least 10% than the recording period corresponding to the maximum sheet-load equipment.

7. *Lighting and protection*
7.1. The visual instruments of the equipment must be provided with adequate non-dazzling lighting.
7.2. For normal conditions of use all the internal parts of the equipment must be protected against damp and dust. In addition they must be made proof against tampering by means of casings capable of being sealed.

(b) **Visual instruments**

1. *Distance travelled indicator (distance recorder)*
1.1. The value of the smallest grading on the instrument showing distance travelled must be 0,1 kilometres. Figures showing hectometres must be clearly distinguishable from those showing whole kilometres.
1.2. The figures on the distance recorder must be clearly legible and must have an apparent height of at least 4mm.
1.3. The distance recorder must be capable of reading up to at least 99 999,9 kilometres.

2. *Speed indicators (speedometer)*
2.1. Within the range of measurement the speed scale must be uniformly graduated by 1, 2, 5, or 10 kilometres per hour. The value of a speed graduation (space between two successive marks) must not exceed 10% of the maximum speed shown on the scale.
2.2. The range indicated beyond that measured need not be marked by figures.
2.3. The length of each space on the scale representing a speed difference of 10 kilometres per hour must not be less than 10 millimetres.
2.4. On an indicator with a needle the distance between the needle and the instrument face must not exceed three millimetres.

3. *Time indicator (clock)*
    The time indicator must be visible from outside the equipment and give a clear, plain and unambiguous reading.

(c) **Recording instruments**

1. *General points*
1.1. All equipment whatever the form of the record sheet (strip or disc) must be provided with a mark enabling the record sheet to be inserted correctly in such a way as to ensure that the time shown by the clock and the time-marking on the sheet correspond.
1.2. The mechanism moving the record sheet must be such as to ensure that the latter moves without play and can be freely inserted and removed.
1.3. For record sheets in disc form the forward movement device must be controlled by the clock mechanism. In this case, the rotating movement of the sheet must be continuous and uniform with a minimum speed of seven millimetres per hour measured at the inner border of the ring marking the edge of the speed recording area.
    In equipment of the strip type where the forward movement device of the sheets is controlled by the clock mechanism the speed of rectilinear forward movement must be at least 10 millimetres per hour.
1.4. Recording of the distances travelled, of the speed of the vehicle and of any opening of the case containing the record sheet or sheets must be automatic.

2. Recording distance travelled

2.1. Every kilometre of distance travelled must be represented on the record by a variation of at least one millimetre on the corresponding coordinate.

2.2. Even at speeds reaching the upper limit of the range of measurement the record of distances must still be clearly legible.

3. Recording speed

3.1. Whatever the form of the record sheet, the speed recording stylus must normally move in a straight line and at right angles to the direction of travel of the record sheet.

However the movement of the stylus may be curvilinear provided that following conditions are satisfied:

 – the trace drawn by the stylus must be perpendicular to the average circumference (in the case of sheets in disc form) or to the axis (in the case of sheets in strip form) of the area reserved for speed recording
 – the ratio between the the radius of curvature of the trace drawn by the stylus and the width of the area reserved for speed recording must be not less than 2.4 to 1 whatever the form of the record sheet.
 – the markings on the time-scale must cross the recording area in a curve of the same radius as the trace drawn by the stylus. The spaces between the markings on the time-scale must represent a period not exceeding one hour.

3.2. Each variation in speed of 10 kilometres per hour must be represented on the record by a variation of at least 1.5 millimetres on the corresponding coordinate.

4. Recording time

4.1. Recording equipment must be so constructed that it is possible, through the operation where necessary of a switch device, to record automatically and separately four periods of time as indicated in Article 15 of the Regulation.

4.2. It must be possible, from the characteristics of the traces, their relative positions and if necessary the signs laid down in Article 15 of the Regulation to distinguish clearly between the various periods of time.

The various periods of time should be differentiated from one or another on the record by differences in the thickness of the relevant traces or by any other system of at least equal effectiveness from the point of view of legibility and ease of interpretation of the record.

4.3. In the case of vehicles with a crew consisting of more than one driver the recordings provided for in point 4.1. must be made on two separate sheets, each sheet being allocated to one driver . In this case, the forward movement of the separate sheets must be effected either by a single mechanism or by separate synchronised mechanisms.

(d) **Closing device**

1. The case containing the record sheet or sheets and the control of the mechanism for resetting the clock must be provided with a clock.

2. Each opening of the case containing the record sheet or sheets and the control of the mechanism for resetting the clock must be automatically recorded on the sheet or sheets.

(e) **Markings**

1. The following markings must appear on the instrument face of the equipment;

    – close to the figure shown by the distance recorder the unit of measurement of distance indicated by the abbreviation 'km',

    – near the speed scale the marking 'km/h',

    – the measurement range of the speedometer in the form 'Vmin...km/h, Vmax...km/h'. This marking is not necessary if it is shown on the descriptive plaque of the equipment.

    However, these requirements shall not apply to recording equipment approved before 10 August 1970.

2. The descriptive plaque must be built into the equipment and must show the following markings, which must be visible on the equipment when installed;

    – name and address of the manufacturer of the equipment,

    – manufacturer's number and year of construction,

    – approval mark for the approval type,

    – the constant of the equipment in the form 'k = ...rev/km' or 'k = ...imp/km',

    – optionally the range of speed measurement, in the form indicated in point 1,

    – should the sensitivity of the instrument to the angle of inclination be capable of affecting the readings given by the equipment beyond the permitted tolerances the permissible angle expressed as:

    where a is the angle measured from the horizontal position of the front face (fitted the right way up) of the equipment for which the instrument is calibrated, while $+B$ and $-Y$ represent respectively the maximum permissible upward and downward deviations from the angle of calibration a.

(f) **Maximum tolerances (visual and recording instruments)**

1. On the test bench before installation:
    (a) distance travelled;
        1% more or less than the real distance where that distance is at least one kilometre;
    (b) speed:
        3km/h more or less than the real speed;
    (c) time:
        + two minutes per day with a maximum of 10 minutes per seven days in cases where the running period of the clock after rewinding is not less than that period.

2. On installation:
    (a) distance travelled:
        2% more or less than the real distance, where that distance is at least one kilometre;
    (b) speed:
        4 km/h more or less than the real speed;
    (c) time:
        + two minutes per day, or
        + 10 minutes per seven days.

3. In use:
    (a) distance travelled:
        4% more or less than the real distance, where that distance is at least one kilometre;

(b) speed:

6 km/h more or less than the real speed;

(c) time:

+ two minutes per day, or

+ 10 minutes per seven days.

4. The maximum tolerances set out in points 1, 2 and 3 are valid for temperatures between 0° and 40° C, temperatures being taken in close proximity to the equipment.

5. Measures of the maximum tolerances set out in points 2 and 3 shall take under the conditions laid down in Chapter V1.

IV RECORD SHEETS

(a) General points

1. The record sheets must be such that they do not impede the normal functioning of the instrument and that the records which they contain are indelible and easily legible and identifiable.

   The record sheets must retain their dimension and any records made on them under normal conditions of humidity and temperature.

   In addition it must be possible to write on the sheets, without damaging them and without affecting the legibility of the recordings, the information referred to in Article 15 (5) of the Regulation.

   Under normal conditions of storage, the recordings must remain clearly legible for at least one year.

2. The minimum recording capacity of the sheets, whatever their form, must be 24 hours.

   If several discs are linked together to increase the continuous recording capacity which can be achieved without intervention by staff, the links between the various discs must be made in such a way that there are no breaks in or overlapping of recordings at the point of transfer from one disc to another.

(b) Recording areas and their graduation

1. The record sheets shall include the following recording areas:

   – an area exclusively reserved for data relating to speed,
   – an area exclusively reserved for data relating to distance travelled,
   – one or more areas for data relating to driving time, to other periods of work and availability to breaks from work and to rest periods for drivers.

2. The area for recording speed must be scaled off in divisions of 20 kilometres per hour or less. The speed corresponding to each marking on the scale must be shown on figures against that marking. The symbol 'km/h' must be shown at least once within the area. The last marking on the scale must coincide with the upper limit of the range of measurement.

3. The area for recording distance travelled must be set out in such a way that the number of kilometres travelled may be read without difficulty.

4. The area or areas reserved for recording the periods referred to in point 1 must be so marked that it is possible to distinguish clearly between the various periods of time.

(c) **Information to be printed on the record sheets**

Each sheet must bear, in printed form, the following information;
  – name and address or trade name of the manufacturer,
  – approval mark for the model of the sheet,
  – approval mark for the type or types of equipment in which the sheet may be used,
  – upper limit of the speed measurement range, printed in kilometres per hour.

By way of minimal additional requirements, each sheet must bear, in printed form a time-scale graduated in such a way that the time may be read directly at intervals of fifteen minutes while each five minute interval may be determined without difficulty.

(d) **Free space for hand written insertions**

A free space must be provided on the sheets such that drivers may as a minimum write in the following details:
  – surname and first name of the driver,
  – date and place where use of the sheet begins and date and place where such use ends,
  – the registration number or numbers of the vehicle or vehicles to which the driver is assigned during the use of the sheet,
  – odometer readings from the vehicle or vehicles to which the driver is assigned during the use of the sheet,
  – the time at which any change of vehicle takes place.

V INSTALLATION OF RECORDING EQUIPMENT

1. Recording equipment must be positioned in the vehicle in such a way that the driver has a clear view from his seat of speedometer, distance recorder and clock while at the same time all parts of those instruments, including driving parts, are protected against accidental damage.
2. It must be possible to adapt the constant of the recording equipment to the characteristic coefficient of the vehicle by means of a suitable device, to be known as an adaptor.

    Vehicles with two or more rear axle ratios must be fitted with a switch device whereby these various ratios may be automatically brought into line with the ratio for which the equipment has been adapted to the vehicle.
3. After the equipment has been checked on installation, an installation plaque shall be affixed to the vehicle beside the equipment or in the equipment itself and in such a way as to be clearly visible. After every inspection by an approved fitter or workshop requiring a change in the setting of the installation itself, a new plaque must be affixed in place of the previous one.

    The plaque must show at least the following details:

    – name, address or trade name of the approved fitter or workshop,
    – characteristic coefficient of the vehicle, in the form 'w = ... rev/km' or 'w = ... imp/km',
    – effective circumference of the wheel tyres in the form 'l = ...mm',
    – the dates on which the characteristic coefficient of the vehicle was determined and the effective measured circumference of the wheel tyres.

4. *Sealing*
The following parts must be sealed;

(a) the installation plaque, unless it is attached in such a way that it cannot be removed without the markings thereon being destroyed;
(b) the two ends of the link between the recording equipment proper and the vehicle;
(c) the adaptor itself and the point of its insertion into the circuit;
(d) the switch mechanism for vehicles with two or more axle ratios;
(e) the links joining the adaptor and the switch mechanism to the equipment;
(f) the casings required under Chapter III (a) 7.2.

In particular cases, further seals may be required on approval of the equipment type and a note of the positioning of these seals must be made on the approval certificate.

Only the seals mentioned in (b), (c) and (e) may be removed in cases of emergency; for each occasion that these seals are broken a written statement giving the reasons for such action must be prepared and made available to the competent authority.

VI CHECKS AND INSPECTIONS

The Member States shall nominate the bodies which shall carry out the checks and inspections.

1. *Certification of new or repaired instruments*
Every individual device, whether new or repaired, shall be certified in respect of its correct operation and the accuracy of its readings and recordings, within the limits laid down in Chapter III (f) 1, by means of sealing in accordance with Chapter V (4) (f).

For this purpose the Member States may stipulate an initial verification, consisting of a check on and confirmation of the conformity of a new or repaired device with the type-approved model and/or with the requirements of the Regulation and its Annexes, or may delegate the power to certify to the manufacturers or to their authorised agents.

2. *Installation*
When being fitted to a vehicle, the equipment and the whole installation must comply with the provisions relating to maximum tolerances laid down in Chapter III (f) 2.

The inspection tests shall be carried out by the approved fitter or workshop on his or its responsibility.

3. *Periodic inspections*
(a) Periodic inspections of the equipment fitted to vehicles shall take place at least every two years and may be carried out in conjunction with roadworthiness tests of vehicles.

These inspections shall include the following checks;
 – that the equipment is working correctly,
 – that the equipment carries the type approval mark,
 – that the installation plaque is affixed,
 – that the seals on the equipment and on the other parts of the installation are intact,
 – the actual circumference of the tyres.
(b) An inspection to ensure compliance with the provision of Chapter III (f) 3 on the maximum tolerances in use shall be carried out at least once every six years, although each Member State may stipulate a shorter interval or such inspection in respect of vehicles registered in its territory. Such inspections must include replacement of the installation plaque.

4. *Measurement of errors*

The measurement of errors on installation and during use shall be carried out under the following conditions, which are to be regarded as constituting standard test conditions;

- vehicle unladen, in normal running order,
- tyre pressures in accordance with the manufacturer's instructions,
- tyre wear within the limits allowed by law,
- movement of the vehicle: the vehicle must proceed, driven by its own engine, in a straight line and on a level surface, at a speed of 50 5 km/h; provided that it is of comparable accuracy, the test may also be carried out on an appropriate test bench.

ANNEX II

APPROVAL MARK AND CERTIFICATE

I APPROVAL MARK

1. The approval mark shall be made up of:

- a rectangle, within which shall be placed the letter 'e' followed by a distinguishing number or letter for the country which has issued the approval in accordance with the following conventional signs:

Belgium	6,
Denmark	18,
Germany	1,
Greece	GR
Spain	9,
France	2,
Ireland	IRE,
Italy	3,
Luxembourg	13,
Netherlands	4,
Portugal	21,
United Kingdom	11,

and

- an approval number corresponding to the number of the approval certificate drawn up for the prototype of the recording equipment or the record sheet, placed at any point within the immediate proximity of this rectangle.

2. The approval mark shall be shown on the descriptive plaque of each set of equipment and on each record sheet. It must be indelible and must always remain clearly legible.

3. The dimensions of the approval mark drawn below are expressed in millimetres, these dimensions being minima. The ratio between the dimensions must be maintained.

II APPROVAL CERTIFICATE

A State having granted approval shall issue the applicant with an approval certificate, the model for which is given below. When informing other Member States of approvals issued or, if the occasion should arise withdrawn, a Member State shall use copies of that certificate.

Approval Certificate

Name of competent administration . . . .

Notification concerning (*)
- approval of a type of recording equipment
- withdrawal of approval of a type of recording equipment
- approval of a record sheet
- withdrawal of approval of a record sheet

. . . .

Approval No . . . .

1. Trade mark or name . . . .
2. Name of type or model . . . .
3. Name of manufacturer . . . .
4. Address of manufacturer . . . .
. . . .
5. Submitted for approval on . . . .
6. Tested at . . . .
7. Date and number of test report. . . . .
8. Date of approval . . . .
9. Date of withdrawal of approval. . . . .
10. Type or types of recording equipment in which sheet is designed to be used . . . .
. . . .
11. Place . . . .
12. Date . . . .
13. Descriptive documents annexed . . . .

---

14. Remarks

. . . .
(Signature)

(*) Delete items not applicable

Note: This Council Regulation (EEC) No 3821/85 is reproduced from the Official Journal of the European Communities No L 370/8 dated December 31, 1985

Appendix II

Exemptions from Tachograph Fitment and Use (UK Derogations)

The EC drivers' hours regulations (ie EC 3820/85) specify a number of exemptions to the hours' law and, consequently, to the need for the fitment and use of tachographs. Additionally, national governments (eg the British government) are permitted to make certain further exemptions (derogations) for operations in their own national territories if they so wish. All of these exemptions and the derogations applicable in the UK are shown below.

International Exemptions (under EC 3820/85 Article 4)

1. Vehicles not exceeding 3.5 tonnes maximum permissible weight including the weight of any trailer or semi-trailer drawn.
2. Passenger vehicles constructed and equipped (and intended) to carry not more than nine persons including driver.
3. Vehicles used for regular passenger services on routes not exceeding 50 kilometres.
4. Vehicles with legal maximum speed not exceeding 30kph (approx 18.6mph).
5. Vehicles used by or under the control of the armed services, civil defence, fire services and forces responsible for maintaining public order.
6. Vehicles used in connection with sewerage, flood protection, water, gas and electricity services, highway maintenance and control, refuse collection and disposal, telephone and telegraph services, carriage of postal articles, radio and television broadcasting and the detection of radio or television transmitters or receivers.
7. Vehicles used in emergencies or rescue operations.
8. Specialised vehicles used for medical purposes.
9. Vehicles transporting circus and funfair equipment.
10. Specialised breakdown vehicles.
11. Vehicles undergoing road tests for technical development, repair or maintenance purposes, and new or rebuilt vehicles which have not yet been put into service.
12. Vehicles used for non-commercial carriage of goods for personal use (ie private use).
13. Vehicles used for milk collection from farms and the return to farms of milk containers or milk products intended for animal feed.

National Exemptions (under EC 3820/85 Article 13 and the Community Drivers' Hours and Recording Equipment (Exemptions and Supplementary Provisions) Regulations 1986– SI 1456/1986– as amended)

1. Passenger vehicles constructed and equipped (and intended) to carry not more than 17 persons including driver.
2. Vehicles used by public authorities to provide public services which are not in competition with professional road hauliers (see note below).

3. Vehicles used by agricultural, horticultural, forestry or fishery* undertakings, for carrying goods within a 50 kilometre radius of the place where the vehicle is normally based, including local administrative areas the centres of which are situated within that radius.

    * *to gain this exemption the vehicle must be used to carry live fish or to carry a catch of fish which has not been subjected to any process or treatment (other than freezing) from the place of landing to a place where it is to be processed or treated.*

4. Vehicles used for carrying animal waste or carcasses not intended for human consumption.
5. Vehicles used for carrying live animals from farms to local markets and vice versa, or from markets to local slaughterhouses.
6. Vehicles specially fitted for and used:

    – as shops at local markets and for door-to-door selling
    – for mobile banking, exchange or savings transactions
    – for worship
    – for the lending of books, records or cassettes
    – for cultural events or exhibitions.

7. Vehicles (not exceeding 7.5 tonnes gvw in UK) carrying material or equipment for the driver's use in the course of his work within 50-kilometre radius of the place where the vehicle is normally based, provided that driving the vehicle does not constitute the driver's main activity and does not seriously prejudice the objectives of the regulations.
8. Vehicles operating exclusively on islands not exceeding 2,300 square kilometres in area which are not linked to the mainland by bridge, ford or tunnel open for use by motor vehicles (excludes Isle of Wight).
9. Vehicles (not exceeding 7.5 tonnes gvw) used for the carriage of goods and propelled by gas produced on the vehicle or by electricity.
10. Vehicles used for driving instruction (but not if carrying goods for hire or reward).
11. Tractors used after 1 January 1990 exclusively for agricultural and forestry work.
12. Vehicles used by the RNLI for hauling lifeboats.
13. Vehicles manufactured before 1 January 1947.
14. Steam propelled vehicles.

Note: In exemption 2 above relating to vehicles used by public authorities, the exemption applies only if the vehicle is being used by:
    (a) a health authority in England and Wales or a health board in Scotland
        – to provide ambulance services in pursuance of its duty under the NHS Act 1977 or NHS (Scotland) Act 1978; or
        – to carry staff, patients, medical supplies or equipment in pursuance of its general duties under the Act;
    (b) a local authority to fulfil social services functions, such as services for old persons or for physically and mentally handicapped persons;
    (c) HM Coastguard or lighthouse authorities;
    (d) harbour authorities within harbour limits;
    (e) airports authority within airport perimeters;
    (f) British Rail, London Regional Transport, a Passenger Transport Executive or local authority for maintaining railways;
    (g) British Waterways Board for maintaining navigable waterways.

Further exemptions are made under British legislation (SI 1456/1986 & 805/1987) as follows:

- passenger vehicles on regular national services,
- passenger vehicles on regular international services with routes not over 100 kilometres and with terminals within 50 kilometres of a frontier between member states,
- vehicles used for collecting sea coal,
- vehicles (other than those not exceeding 3.5 tonnes maximum permissible weight {mpw}) used for the carriage of postal articles other than letters as follows; those not exceeding 7.5 tonnes mpw to be fitted by January 1, 1990, those exceeding 7.5 tonnes mpw to be fitted from April 1, 1988.

Appendix III

Summary of EC Drivers' Hours Law (EC 3820/85)

European Communities Regulation 3820/85, which repealed previous regulations (EC 543/69 as amended), changed many of the previous requirements relating to driving times, breaks and rest periods and made fundamental changes to some aspects of the basic structure of the rules. To be able to apply the rules as required and appreciate their implications it is necessary to understand the definitions of certain words and phrases used as follows:

Crew Members
The regulations apply specifically to the 'driver' of the vehicle and not to 'crew members' as before. For these purposes a 'driver' is any person who drives the vehicle, even for a short period, or who is carried in the vehicle in order to be available for driving if necessary.

Vehicle Categories
The previous distinction between the so-called category 1 and category 2 vehicles (ie Article 6 and non-Article 6 vehicles in EC 543/69), for the purposes of determining extended daily driving and break period requirements, is abolished. Drivers of all types of vehicles within the scope of the regulations are treated equally in regard to driving, break and rest periods.

A Day
For the purposes of the regulations a day is any period of 24 hours, in other words a rolling period. If a driver drives a vehicle to which the EC regulations apply on any day then the legal requirements apply to him for that day and the week in which that day falls.

Fixed Week
The definition of a 'week' for these purposes is a fixed week from 00.00 hours Monday to 24.00 hours on the following Sunday. All references in the rules to weeks and weekly limits must be considered against this fixed week.

Driving
Driving is time spent behind the wheel actually driving the vehicle, unlike the previous interpretation where driving could include other periods of work activity sandwiched between driving periods. Thus 'driving' relates to an accumulation of periods spent driving before a break is needed and does not aggregate with 'work' stops. The maximum limit for driving before a break is taken is four and a half hours.

Driving Limits

Goods vehicle drivers are restricted under the regulations in the amount of time they can spend driving before taking a break, driving in a day, in a week and in a fortnight. The maximum limits are as follows:

Maximum aggregated driving before a break:	$4\frac{1}{2}$ hours
Maximum daily driving:	
normally:	9 hours
extension:	10 hours on 2 days in the week
Maximum weekly driving:	6 daily driving shifts (see note p 185)
Maximum fortnightly driving:	90 hours

NB: It should be noted that where a driver spends the maximum amount of driving time behind the wheel in one week (ie 4×9 hours plus 2×10 hours = 56 hours), during the following fixed week he may drive for a maximum of only 34 hours.

Break Periods

Drivers are required by law to take a break or breaks if in a day the aggregate of their driving time amounts to $4\frac{1}{2}$ hours or more. If the driver does not drive for periods amounting in aggregate to $4\frac{1}{2}$ hours in the day there is no legal requirement for him to take a break during that day. Break periods must not be regarded as part or parts of a daily rest period and during breaks the driver must not carry out any 'other work'. However, waiting time, time spent riding as passenger in a vehicle or time spent on a ferry or train are not counted as 'other work' for these purposes.

The requirement for taking a break is that immediately the four and a half hour driving limit is reached a break of 45 minutes must be taken. This break may be replaced by a number of other breaks of at least 15 minutes each distributed over the driving period or taken during and immediately after this period, so as to equal at least 45 minutes. A break period which was otherwise due in accordance with this requirement does not have to be taken if immediately following the driving period the driver commences a daily or weekly rest period, so long as the four and a half hours' aggregated driving is not exceeded.

NB: It is important to note that break periods (ie either 15 minute or 45 minute periods) should not be curtailed even by a minute or two. Prosecutions have been brought for break periods which are alleged not to conform to the law even though they have been only a matter of minutes below the minimums specified in the regulations.

Rest periods

Rest periods are uninterrupted periods of at least one hour during which the driver 'may freely dispose of his time'. Daily rest periods, and particularly rest periods which are compensating for previously reduced rest periods, should not be confused with, or combined with, statutory break periods required to be taken during the driving day.

Daily Rest Periods

Drivers are required to observe a normal, reduced or split daily rest period during which time they must be free to dispose of their time as they wish. In each 24-hour period the following rest periods must be taken:

Normally:	11 hours
or	
Reduced rest:	9 hours – may be taken three times in a week but the reduced time must be compensated by an equal amount of time taken before the end of the next following fixed week

Split rest: Where the daily rest period is not reduced (as above) the rest may be split and taken in two or three periods during the 24 hours, provided:

(a) one continuous period is of at least 8 hours' duration;
(b) other periods are of at least one hour's duration;
(c) the total daily rest period is increased to 12 hours.

Double-manned Vehicles

Where a vehicle is operated by a two-man crew, the daily rest period requirement is that each man must have had a minimum of eight hours' rest in each period of 30 hours.

Daily Rest on Vehicles

Daily rest periods may be taken on a vehicle provided:

(a) the vehicle has a bunk
(b) the vehicle is stationary.

It follows from this that a driver on a double-manned vehicle cannot be taking part of his daily rest period on the bunk while his co-driver continues to drive the vehicle. He could, however, be taking a break at this time.

Daily Rest on Ferries/Trains

Daily rest periods which are taken when a ferry crossing or rail journey is involved may be interrupted once only, provided:

(a) part of the rest is taken on land before or after the crossing/rail journey;
(b) the interruption must be 'as short as possible' and in any event must not be more than one hour before embarkation or after disembarkation and this time must include dealing with customs formalities;
(c) during both parts of the rest (ie in the terminal and on board the ferry/train) the driver must have access to a bunk or couchette;
(d) when such interruptions to daily rest occur, the total daily rest period must be extended by two hours.

Weekly Rest Period

Once each fixed week (and after six daily driving periods) a daily rest period must be combined with a weekly rest period to provide a total continuous rest period of 45 hours. A weekly rest period which begins in one fixed week and continues into the following week may be attached to either of these weeks.
Weekly rest periods may be reduced to:

(a) 38 hours when taken at the place where vehicle or the driver is based;
(b) 24 hours when taken elsewhere.

Reduced weekly rest periods must be compensated (ie made up) by an equivalent amount of time taken en-bloc before the end of the third week following the week in which the reduced weekly rest period is taken.

Compensated Rest Periods

When reduced daily and/or weekly rest periods are taken, the compensated time must be attached to another rest period of at least eight hours' duration and must be granted, at the request of the driver, at the vehicle parking place or at the driver's base.

Summary of EC Rules

The following table summarises the EC rules applicable to both national and international goods vehicle operations:

Daily driving:	9 hours
	10 hours on 2 days in week
Weekly driving:	6 daily driving periods★
Fortnightly driving:	90 hours
Maximum driving before a break:	4½ hours
Minimum breaks after driving:	45 minutes or other breaks of at least 15 minutes each
Daily rest:	11 hours
Reduced daily rest:	9 hours on up to 3 days per week (must be made up by end of next following week)
Split daily rest:	The 11-hour daily rest period may be split into 2 or 3 periods
	– one at least 8 hours
	– others at least one hour each –
	– total rest increased to 12 hours
Weekly rest:	45 hours once each fixed week
Reduced weekly rest:	36 hours at base – 24 hours elsewhere (any reduction must be made up *en-bloc* by end of 3rd following week)
Rest on ferries/trains:	May be interrupted once only if:
	– part taken on land
	– no more than 1 hour between parts
	– drivers must have access to bunk/couchette
	– total rest must increase by 2 hours

NB: The British High Court ruled in 1988 that in the UK drivers can exceed the maximum of six daily driving shifts within six days as specified in the EC rules provided they do not exceed the maximum number of hours permitted in six consecutive driving periods (ie 54 hours normally but may be 56 hours if two 10-hour driving days are included as permitted or only 34 hours if the full 56 hours was driven in the preceding week so as not to exceed the 90-hour two-weekly total).

Emergencies

It is permitted for the driver to depart from the EC rules to the extent necessary to enable him to reach a suitable stopping place when emergencies arise where he needs to ensure the safety of persons, the vehicle or its load, providing road safety is not jeopardised. The nature of and reasons for departing from the rules in these circumstances must be shown on the tachograph chart.

Appendix IV

Bibliography of Relevant UK Legislation

The following legislation is applicable in the UK in regard to both restriction on goods and passenger vehicle driving and the fitment and use of tachographs in goods and passenger vehicles:

1. *Transport Act 1968* (Part VI contains original UK legislation on drivers' hours and tachographs)
2. *European Communities Act 1972*
3. *Road Traffic (Drivers' Ages and Hours of Work) Act 1976*
4. *Transport Act 1978*
5. *The Drivers' Hours (Goods Vehicles) (Modifications) Order 1970* (SI 257/1970)
6. *The Drivers' Hours (Passenger and Goods Vehicles) (Modifications)* Order 1971 (SI 818/1971)
7. *The Passenger and Goods Vehicles (Recording Equipment) Regulations 1979/1981/1984* (SI 1746/81 - 1692//81 - 144/84)
8. *EC Regulation 3820/85* (covering drivers' hours)
9. *EC Regulation 3821/85* (covering tachograph fitment and use)
10. *The Community Drivers' Hours and Recording Equipment Regulations 1986* (SI 1457/1986)
11. *The Community Drivers' Hours and Recording Equipment (Exemptions and Supplementary Provisions) Regulations 1986* as amended (implements EC regulations in UK and the derogations) (see Appendix II) (SI 1456 – 1669/86 – 805/87)
12. *The Drivers' Hours (Goods Vehicles) (Modifications) Order 1986* (which implements changes to national and domestic driving under 1968 Act) (SI 1459/1986)
13. *The Drivers' Hours (Harmonisation with Community Rules) Regulations 1986* (which harmonise rules for those who drive under both EC and UK Domestic – ie 1968 Act – provisions) (SI 1458/1986)
14. *The Drivers' Hours (Goods Vehicles) (Exemptions) Regulations 1986* (revokes earlier 'special needs' concessions and emergency exemption) (SI 1492/1986)
15. *The Drivers' Hours (Goods Vehicles) (Keeping of Records) Regulations 1987* (deals with record books for EC exempt operations within scope of 1968 Transport Act – ie British Domestic driving) (SI 1421/1987)
16. *European Agreement concerning the Work of Crews of Vehicles engaged in International Road Transport (AETR)*

Appendix V

Tachographs and UK Annual Vehicle Testing

Examination of the tachograph is part of the annual heavy goods vehicle test in the UK under The Goods Vehicles (Plating and Testing) Regulations 1988. Under these regulations any heavy goods vehicle presented for its annual test will have its tachograph installation inspected at the Goods Vehicle Test Station in accordance with item 29 in the *Goods Vehicle Tester's Manual* (current – 1984 edition) as follows:

Method of Inspection

This inspection applies to all vehicles required to have a tachograph or where one is fitted in place of a speedometer.

1. Check that a tachograph is fitted.
2. Check that the tachograph can easily be seen from the driving seat.
3. Check the condition of the tachograph.
4. Check that the tachograph can be illuminated.
5. Check all seals for presence and condition (see note).

NOTE : If a tachograph is fitted but the vehicle is exempt from the Regulations then Method of Inspection item No 5 does not apply.

Reasons for Rejection

1. Tachograph not fitted, not complete or clearly inoperative.
2. Tachograph cannot easily be seen by a person sitting in the driving seat.
3. Tachograph cannot be illuminated, so that it can be seen in the hours of darkness by a person sitting in the driving seat.
4. Tachograph dial glass broken or missing (see Note 1).
5. A seal missing or defective (see Note 2).

NOTE 1. It is not considered a failure if the dial glass is cracked, provided there is no possibility of misreading or of the needle fouling and there is not a safety hazard.
NOTE 2. If a tachograph is fitted but the vehicle is exempt from the regulations, Reason for Rejection No 5 does not apply.

TACHOGRAPHS – DECLARATION OF EXEMPTION

Station Manager
Heavy Goods Vehicle Testing Station
. . . .
. . . .
I declare that vehicle Reg No . . . . which is owned by . . . .
is exempt from having a tachograph fitted, for the reason shown below
(please tick as appropriate)
Signed . . . .
Name (in capitals). . . . .
Status . . . .
Date . . . .
Vehicle below 3.5 tonnes permissible maximum weight
Vehicle not used for the carriage of goods
Vehicle privately owned and driven (eg private horse box)
Vehicle used by the police, armed forces, fire brigade, civil defence, drainage or flood-prevention authorities, water, gas or electricity services, highway authorities, and refuse collection, telegraph or telephone services, by the postal authorities for the carriage of mail, by radio or television services or for the detection of radio or television transmitters or receivers or a vehicle which is used by other public authorities for public services and which are not in competition with professional road hauliers
Vehicle used for the carriage of sick or injured persons and for carrying rescue materials, and any other specialised vehicle used for medical purposes
Tractor with a maximum authorised speed not exceeding 30 kilometres per hour
Tractor or other machine used exclusively for local agricultural and forestry work
Vehicle used to transport circus and fun-fair equipment
Specialised breakdown vehicle
*Specialised vehicle at local markets
*Specialised vehicle for door-to-door selling
*Specialised vehicle for mobile banking, exchange or savings transactions
*Specialised vehicle for the purpose of worship
*Specialised vehicle for the lending of books, records or cassettes
*Specialised vehicle for cultural events
*Specialised vehicle for mobile exhibitions
*Vehicle used for the transport of live animals from farms to local markets and vice versa and transport of animals' carcases or waste not intended for human consumption.

PLEASE NOTE that this form will be sent to your Traffic Area Office following the test for the information of the enforcement staff who, in cases of doubt, may wish to discuss with you the reasons for this exemption declaration.

*These exemptions do not apply to international journeys.

Form to be filled in when presenting a vehicle for annual test when exemption from tachograph fitment and use is claimed.

Appendix VI

Approved Tachograph Centres in the UK

The following are Department of Transport approved Tachograph Centres (ie workshops as referred to in EC legislation) in the UK based on lists issued and updated from time to time by the DTp. The list is categorised by the county, region or island in which they are located and provides the DTp code reference for each centre. This list is believed to be correct at the time of going to press on the basis of the DTp official listing dated September 1988.

*Remote area centres are shown with an asterisk

ENGLAND

AVON

BRISTOL GB H 105
Swan National Motors (Bristol) Ltd
Coventry & Jeffs
Anchor Road
Bristol BS1 5TT
Tel: 0272 20031

BRISTOL GB H 117
Evans Halshaw SW Ltd
Avonmouth Way
Avonmouth
Bristol BS11 8DB
Tel: 0272 824611

BRISTOL GB H 118
AD Forsey (Transport) Ltd
Weston Super Mare Motors
Days Road
Barton Hill
Bristol BS5 0AI
Tel: 0272 551571

BRISTOL GB H 201
Lex Tillotson Bristol
High Street
Kingswood
Bristol BS15 4AH
Tel: 0272 677841

BRISTOL GB H 222
Lex Tillotson Bristol
Days Road
St Phillips
Bristol BS2 0OP
Tel: 0272 557755

BRISTOL GB H 202
Bryan Bros. Trucks Ltd
Albert Crescent
St Phillips
Bristol BS2 0UD
Tel: 0272 772671

BRISTOL GB H 216
SA Trucks (Bristol) Ltd
Third Way
Avonmouth
Bristol BS11 9YL
Tel: 0272 821241

BRISTOL GB H 303
Moreys Daf Trucks Ltd
T/A ATAC
Unit 3B
Severnside Trading Estate
St Andrews Road
Avonmouth
Bristol BS11 9YS
Tel: 0272 828583

BRISTOL GB H 314
Welch and Company Ltd
Avon Street
Bristol BS2 0PZ
Tel: 0272 770411

CHIPPING SODBURY GB H 110
Dando's (Motor Services) Ltd
Hatters Lane
Bridge Road Works
Chipping Sodbury BS17 6AS
Tel: 0454 318187

WESTON-SUPER-MARE GB H 313
Weston-Super-Mare Motors
Bridge Road Works
Weston-Super-Mare BS23 3NF
Tel: 0934 28127

BEDFORDSHIRE

BEDFORD GB F 105
Charles King (Motors) Ltd
Hudson Road
Elms Farm Industrial Estate
Bedford MK41 0JQ
Tel: 0234 40041

BEDFORD GB D 208
Arlington Motor Co Ltd
The Embankment
Barkers Lane
Bedford MK41 9SD
Tel: 0234 270000

BEDFORD GB F 303
Servoway Ltd
3 Brunel Road
Barkers Lane Industrial Estate
Bedford MK41 9TL
Tel: 0234 211241

DUNSTABLE GB N 222
Trimoco Ltd
Skimpot Road
Dunstable LU5 4JX
Tel: 0582 597575

LEIGHTON BUZZARD GB E 100
Chassis Developments Ltd
Grovebury Road
Leighton Buzzard LU7 8SL
Tel: 0525 374151

LEIGHTON BUZZARD GB E 315
Dawson Freight Commercials Ltd
Stoneleigh Garage
Billington Road
Leighton Buzzard
Tel: 0525 851851

LUTON
Shaw & Kilburn Ltd
540-550 Dunstable Road
Luton LU4 8DW
Tel: 0582 575944

BERKSHIRE

BRACKNELL GB K 307
John Lewis and Co Ltd.
Central Vehicle Workshop
Doncastle Road
Southern Industrial Area
Bracknell
Tel: 0344 424680

READING GB K 104
Penta Truck and Van Centre
Station Road
Theale RG7 4AG
Tel: 0734 867272

READING GB K 200
Zenith (Reading) Trucks Ltd
20 Commercial Road
Reading RG2 0RN
Tel: 0734 312660

READING GB K 215
Lucas Service UK Ltd
16-20 Long Barn Lane
Reading RG2 7SZ
Tel: 0734 861202

BUCKINGHAMSHIRE

AYLESBURY GB E 202
Perrys Ltd
Griffen Lane
Aylesbury HP19 3BY
Tel: 0296 26162

COLNBROOK GB N 333
Scantruck Ltd
Skyway 14
Calderway (Off Horton Road)
Colnbrook SL3 0BQ

HIGH WYCOMBE GB N 306
Biffa Ltd
Kingsmill
London Road
High Wycombe
Tel: 0494 21221

MILTON KEYNES GB E 216
City Truck Sales Ltd
10, Northfield Drive
Milton Keynes MK15 0DE
Tel: 0908 665152

MILTON KEYNES GB E 306
Perrys Ltd
Clarke Road
Mount Farm Estate
Milton Keynes MK1 1NP
Tel: 0908 74011

CAMBRIDGESHIRE

CAMBRIDGE GB F 100
Marshall (Cambridge) Ltd
Airport Garage
Newmarket Road
Cambridge CB5 8SQ
Tel: 0223 61133

CAMBRIDGE GB F 212
Lucas Service UK Ltd
442 Newmarket Road
Cambridge CB5 8JU
Tel: 0223 315931

CAMBRIDGE GB F 312
Gilbert Rice Ltd
Commercial Vehicle Division
375-381 Milton Road
Cambridge CB4 1SR
Tel: 0223 315959

HUNTINGDON GB F 307
Murkett Bros Ltd
St Mary's Works
Brookside
Huntingdon PE18 6HX
Tel: 0480 52697

HUNTINGDON GB F 108
Ouse Valley Motors
Station Road
St Ives
Huntingdon PE17 4BL
Tel: 0480 62641

PETERBOROUGH GB F 213
Sellers and Batty Ltd
Fengate
Peterborough PE1 5XG
Tel: 0733 60591

PETERBOROUGH GB F 215
T C Harrison Group Ltd
Truck Division
Oxney Road
Peterborough PE1 5YN
Tel: 0733 558111

PETERBOROUGH GB F 315
BRS Midlands Ltd
Fengate Commercials
Nursery Lane
Fengate
Peterborough PE1 5BG
Tel: 0733 65201

PETERBOROUGH GB F 111
Ford and Slater of Peterborough
316 Padholme Road
Peterborough PE1 1BA
Tel: 0733 47100

CHESHIRE

BRETTON GB C 108
H & J Quick Ltd
Premier Garage
Bretton
Nr Chester CH4 0DS
Tel: 0244 660681

CREWE GB C 116
Crewe Tachograph Centre
Chamberlains Transport Ltd
Brodley Road
Haslington
Crewe CW1 1PU
Tel: 0270 581224

ELLESMERE PORT GB C 225
Tachograph Chester Ltd
Rossfield Road
Rossmore Trading Estate
Ellesmere Port L65 3AN
Tel: 051-355 2101

MIDDLEWICH GB C 232
ERF Service Centre
Road Beta
Brooks Lane
Middlewich CW10 0JZ
Tel: 060-684 4711

NORTHWICH GB C 302
North West Truck Engineering Ltd
Griffiths Road
Lostock Gralam
Northwich CW9 7NU
Tel: 0606 48611

SANDBACH GB C 227
Sandbach Truck Centre Ltd
Station Road
Elworth
Sandbach CW11 9JG
Tel: 0270 763291

STALYBRIDGE GB C 233
Tameside Tachograph Centre
Bayfreight Garages
Premier Mill
Tame Street
Stalybridge SK15 1ST

STOCKPORT GB C 202
Gordon Ford Trucks
Greyhound Industrial Estate
Macclesfield Road
Hazel Grove
Stockport SK7 6DB
Tel: 061-456 6333

SUTTON WEAVER GB C 125
Leyfield Commercial Services Ltd
Ashville Way
Sutton Weaver
Nr Runcorn WA7 3EZ

WARRINGTON GB C 221
Irons and Dean Dana Ltd
(Heavy Duty Division)
Units 14-15 Colville Court
Calver Road
Winwick Quay Industrial Estate
Warrington WA2 8QT
Tel: 0925 55251

WARRINGTON GB C 330
Ryland Vehicle Group North West Ltd
Winwick Street Factory
John Street
Warrington WA2 7UD

WARRINGTON GB C 300
C. D. Bramall Ltd
Winwick Road
Dallam Lane
Warrington WA2 7NY
Tel: 0925 51111

WIDNES GB C 226
Irons and Dean Dana Ltd
Moor Lane
Widnes WA8 7AN

WIDNES GB C 321
Sutton & Son (St Helens) Ltd
6 Tanhouse Lane
Widnes WA8 0RZ
Tel: 051-424 3078

CLEVELAND

BILLINGHAM GB B 317
North East DAF Trucks Ltd
Cowpen Bewley Road
Haverton Hill
Billingham TS23 4EX

STOCKTON-ON-TEES GB A 100
Hargreaves Vehicle Distributors Ltd
Bowesfield Lane
Stockton-on-Tees
Tel 0642 614121

STOCKTON-ON-TEES GB A 202
Auto Electrics (Tees-side) Ltd
Thornaby House
Thornaby
Stockton-on-Tees TS17 6BW
Tel: 0642 607901

STOCKTON-ON-TEES GB A 208
Electro Diesel North East Ltd
Portrack Grange Road
Portrack Industrial Estate
Stockton-on-Tees
Tel: 0642 605050

CORNWALL

HELSTON GB H 206
Wincanton Garages Ltd
St Johns
Helston TR13 8EX
Tel: 03265 2561

*LAUNCESTON GB H 214**
Pannell Commercials
Pennygillam Industrial Estate
Launceston PL15 7ED
Tel: 0566 3896/4361

*LAUNCESTON GB H 319**
T H Cawsey Commercials Ltd
Newport Industrial Estate
Launceston PL15 8EX
Tel: 0566 2805

ST. AUSTELL GB H 106
People 2000 Ltd
Slades Road
St. Austell PL25 4HP
Tel: 0724 72333

ST. AUSTELL GB H 212
Heavy Transport (EEC) Ltd
Westhaul Park
Par Moor Road
St Austell PL25 3RA
Tel: 0726 812382/4/5

CUMBRIA

CARLISLE GB A 102
Thomas Armstrong (Transport Services) Ltd
Workington Road
Flimby
Maryport CA15 8RY
Tel: 0900 68114

CARLISLE GB A 303
Carlisle Commercials Ltd
Kingstown Industrial Estate
Kingstown
Carlisle CA2 7NS
Tel: 0228 29262

CARLISLE GB A 304
County Garage Company Ltd
Wakefield Road
Kingstown Estate
Carlisle CA3 0HE
Tel: 0228 24234

*COCKERMOUTH GB A 206**
Gilbraith Commercials Ltd
Trading Estate
Kingstown
Carlisle
Tel: 0228 25422

DERBYSHIRE

CASTLE DONNINGTON GB E 500
BFI Trucks Ltd
Trent Lane
Castle Donnington DE7 2NP
Tel: 0332 811310

DERBY GB E 307
BRS Midlands Ltd
Meadow Lane
Alvaston DE2 8QR
Tel: 0332 71931

DERBY GB E 201
T C Harrison Group Ltd
Chequers Road
Derby DE2 6EN
Tcl: 0332 31188

DERBY GB E 223
F B Atkins & Son Ltd
Burton Road
Findern DE6 6BG
Tel: 0332 516151

DERBY GB E 308
Kays Mackworth Ltd
Ashbourne Road
Mackworth DE3 4 NB
Tel: 0331 24371

DERBY GB E 226
Sherwood Leyland DAF Ltd
Berristowe Lane
Blackwell DE55 5HP
Tel: 0773 863311

DEVON

BARNSTAPLE GB H 100
P M Clarke (Commercials) Ltd
Severn Brethren Trading Estate
Barnstaple
Tel: 0271 45151

BARNSTAPLE GB H 209
S & B (Tachographs) Commercials Devon Ltd
Roundswell Industrail Estate
Old Torrington Road
Barnstaple EX31 3NL
Tel: 0271 76658

EXETER GB H 204
Lucas Service UK Ltd
Grace Road
Exeter EX2 8PE
Tel: 0392 70235

EXETER GB H 213
Frank Tucker (Commercials) Ltd
Peamore Garage
Alphington
Exeter EX2 9SL
Tel: 0392 833030

EXETER GB H 122
Exeter Truck Centre Ltd
Falcon Road
Sowton Industrial Estate
Exeter EX2 7LB
Tel: 0392 79881

EXETER GB H 300
Evans Halshaw SW Ltd
Grace Road
Marsh Barton
Exeter
Tel: 0392 76561

NEWTON ABBOT GB H 305
Newton Abbot Motors Ltd
Bradley Lane
Newton Abbot
Tel: 0626 65081

PLYMOUTH GB H 116
Vospers Trucks Ltd
Hobart Street
Plymouth PL1 3LW
Tel: 0752 668040

PLYMOUTH GB H 211
Heavy Transport (EEC) Ltd
Newham Road
Colebrook
Plympton
Plymouth PL7 4AR
Tel: 0752 335066

PLYMOUTH GB H 310
Plymouth and South Devon Co-operative Society
Ltd
Transport Department
Recreation Road
Peverall
Plymouth
Tel: 0752 787321

DORSET

BOURNEMOUTH GB K 114
Lucas Service UK Ltd
Elliot Road
West Howe Industrial Estate
Bournemouth
Tel: 0202 570507

POOLE GB H 318
Morey Leyland DAF Trucks Ltd
Unit 2
Willis Way
Fleets Industrial Estate
Poole BH15 3SZ
Tel: 0202 675131

POOLE GB K 216
New English Trucks
Unit 2
Willis Way
Fleets Industrial Estate
Poole BH15 3SX
Tel: 0202 671122

DORCHESTER GB H 114
Executors of R W Troop (dec'd)
T/A Bere Regis and District Motor Services
Grove Trading Estate
Dorchester DT1 1RW
Tel: 0305 62992

WEYMOUTH GB H 308
Marsh Road Garages
Marsh Road
Weymouth
Tel: 03057 76116

DURHAM

CHESTER-LE-STREET GB A 106
Grady Hall Ltd
Millbay Vehicle Sales
Drum Road
Chester-Le-Street DH3 2AF
Tel: 091-410 4261

CHESTER-LE-STREET GB A 309
Transfleet Services Ltd
Penshaw Way
Portobello Trading Estate
Birtley
Chester-Le-Street DH3 2SA
Tel: 091-410 4437

DARLINGTON GB A 104
Skipper of Darlington Ltd
Allington Way
Yarm Road Industrial Estate
Darlington
Tel: 0325 59242

DARLINGTON GB A 300
North Riding Garages Ltd
Middleton St. George
Darlington DL2 1HR
Tel: 0325 332941

DARLINGTON GB A 301
Darlington Commercials
Lingfield Way
Yarm Road Industrial Estate
Darlington DL1 4PY

SPENNYMOOR GB A 105
SPD Ltd
Watsons Carriers
Green Lane Industrial Estate
Green Lane
Spennymoor DL16 6DW
Tel: 0388 815900

ESSEX

BASILDON GB N 230
Arlington Commercial Vehicle Sales & Repairs
Cranes Close
Basildon SS14 3JD
Tel: 0268 20223

BENFLEET GB F 102
W Harold Perry Ltd
Stadium Way
Benfleet SS7 3NU

CHELMSFORD GB F 110
Lucas Service UK Ltd
3 Montrose Road
Dukes Park Industrial Estate
Chelmsford CM2 6TE
Tel: 0245 466166

CHELMSFORD GB F 205
Trimoco plc
11 Montrose Road
Dukes Park Industrial Estate
Chelmsford CM2 6TF
Tel: 0245 466619

CHELMSFORD
County Motor Works (Chelmsford) Ltd
Eastern Approach
Springfield
Chelmsford CM2 6PT
Tel: 0245 466333

COLCHESTER GB F 209
Colchester Fuel Injections Ltd
Haven Road
Colchester CO2 8HT
Tel: 0206 862049

COLCHESTER GB F 500
Candor Motors Ltd
114 Ipswich Road
Colchester CO4 4AB

DAGENHAM GB N 229
Unigate Garage
Selinas Lane
Chadwell Heath
Dagenham RH8 10H

GRAYS GB N 329
Harris Commercial Repairs Ltd
601 London Road
West Thurrock
Grays
Tel: 0708 864426

HARLOW GB N 205
Arlington Motor Co. Ltd
Potter Street
Harlow CM17 9NP
Tel: 0279 22391

PURFLEET GB N 206
Scan Truck Ltd
Arterial Road
Purfleet RM16 1TR
Tel: 0708 864915

GLOUCESTERSHIRE

GLOUCESTER GB H 217
Watts Truck Centre Ltd
Mercia Road
Gloucester
Tel: 0452 25721

GLOUCESTER GB H 218
Taylors (Gloucester) Ltd
Bristol Road
Hempstead
Gloucester GL2 6BY
Tel: 0452 21581

GLOUCESTER GB H 120
BRS Western Ltd
St Oswald Road
Gloucester

GLOUCESTER GB H 217
ATAC (Gloucester)
Unit 55a
Gloucester Trading Estate
Hucclecote
Gloucester

TEWKESBURY GB H 111
W. J. Oldacre (Services) Ltd
Northway Trading Estate
Tewkesbury
Tel: 0684 295096

HAMPSHIRE

ALDERSHOT GB K 220
P. D. E. (Farnham) Ltd
Pavilion Road
Aldershot GU11 3NX
Tel: 0252 316504

ALDERSHOT GB K 302
Baker Aldershot
1 Lower Farnham Road
Aldershot GU12 4DZ
Tel: 0252 24401

ANDOVER GB K 109
Spartrucks Ltd
Stephenson Close
Portway Industrial Estate
Andover SP10 3RY
Tel: 0264 66224

BASINGSTOKE GB K 113
Jacksons (Baskingstoke) Ltd
Roentgen Road
Daneshill East Industrial Estate
Basingstoke RG24 0NT
Tel: 0256 461656

EASTLEIGH GB K 100
Hendy Lennox (Southampton) Ltd
Bournemouth Road
Chandlers Ford
Eastleigh SO5 3ZG
Tel: 0703 266388

FAREHAM GB K 119
Spartrucks Ltd
Standard Way
Wallington Industrial Estate
Fareham PO16 8XL
Tel: 0329 286224

PORTSMOUTH GB K 112
Wadham Stringer Commercials
Burrfields Road
Copnor
Portsmouth PO3 5NN
Tel: 0705 664900

PORTSMOUTH GB K 221
Lucas Service UK Ltd
Airport Services Road
Portsmouth PO3 5PY
Tel: 0705 661504

PORTSMOUTH GB K 301
United Services Garage Ltd
Norway Road
Hilsea
Portsmouth
Tel: 0705 661321

SOUTHAMPTON GB K 201
Morey Leyland DAF
The Causeway
Redbridge
Southampton SO9 4YS
Tel: 0703 663000

SOUTHAMPTON GB K 223
Taplin's Auto Electrical Ltd
36/37 St Mary's Street
Southampton SO9 5GE
Tel: 0703 331331

SOUTHAMPTON GB K 304
Bristol Street Motors (Southampton) Ltd
2nd Avenue
Millbrook
Southampton SO1 0LP

SOUTHAMPTON GB K 310
Princes Commercials (Southampton) Ltd
Test Lane
Nursling Industrial Estate
Southampton SO1 9JX
Tel: 0703 701900

HEREFORD & WORCESTER

BROOMHALL GB D 300
Carmichael Trucks Ltd
Bath Road
Broomhall
Worcester WR3 3HR
Tel: 0905 820377

EVESHAM GB D 201
Coulters Garage (Evesham) Ltd
Elm Road
Eversham WR11 5DW
Tel: 0386 47111

HEREFORD GB D 211
Lucas Service UK Ltd
Mortimer Road
Hereford HR4 9JG
Tel: 0432 265571/267678

HEREFORD GB D 302
The Praill Motor Group Ltd
Holmer Road
Hereford HR4 9SD
Tel: 0432 268181

HERTFORDSHIRE

BOREHAMWOOD GB N 302
W H Perry Ltd
Stirling Corner
Stirling Way
Borehamwood WD6 2AX
Tel: 01-207 3100

HATFIELD GB N 217
S & B Commercials Ltd
Huggins Lane Welham Green
Hatfield AL9 7LA
Tel: 07072 61111

HITCHIN GB N 309
Swan Garage (Hitchin) Ltd
Grove Road
Hitchin
Tel: 0462 59744

KINGS LANGLEY GB N 331
E J Masters Ltd
Railway Terrace
Kings Langley WD4 8JA
Tel: 09277 68921

ST ALBANS GB N 310
Godfrey Davis (St. Albans) Ltd
Bricknell Park
St. Albans
Tel: 0727 59155

WATFORD GB N 219
Vales Truck Centre Ltd
Tolpits Lane
Watford WD1 8QP
Tel 0923 776688

HUMBERSIDE

BROUGH GB B 208
Humberside Motors Ltd
Junction 38, M62
Newport
Brough HU15 2RD
Tel: 04302 2297

GOOLE GB B 124
BRS Northern Ltd
Mariner Street
Goole DN14 5BW
Tel: 0405 69639

GRIMSBY GB E 214
Hartford Motors (Grimsby) Ltd
Corporation Road
Grimsby DN31 1UH
Tel: 0472 358941

GRIMSBY GB B 315
T H Brown Ltd
Estate Road One
South Humberside Industrial Estate
Grimsby DN31 2TA
Tel: 0472 46913

HULL GB B 109
Thompson of Hull Ltd
230-236 Anlaby Road
Hull HU3 2RR
Tel: 0482 23681

HULL GB B 110
Crossload Commercials Group
Valletta Street
Hedon Road
Hull HU9 5NP
Tel: 0482 781831

HULL GB B 213
Lex Tillotson (Hull) Ltd
Hedon Road
Hull HU9 5PJ
Tel: 0482 795111

HULL GB B 216
Crystal of Hull Ltd
Little Fair Road
Hedon Road
Hull HU9 5LA
Tel: 0482 25732

HULL GB B 313
Torridan Commercial Vehicles Ltd
Ann Watson Street
Stoneferry
Hull HU8 0BJ
Tel: 0482 839677

SCUNTHORPE GB E 112
BRS Northern Ltd
Grange Lane North
Scunthorpe DN16 1BY
Tel: 0724 280079

SCUNTHORPE GB B 218
H & L Garages Ltd
Grange Lane North
Scunthorpe DN16 1BT
Tel: 0724 856655

SCUNTHORPE GB E 302
Lex Tillotson Scunthorpe
Midland Industrial Estate
Kettering Road
Scunthorpe DN16 1VW
Tel: 0724 282444

SOUTH KILLINGHOLME GB E 219
H & L Garages Ltd
Humber Road
South Killingholme DN40 3DL
Tel: 0469 571666

ISLE OF WIGHT

NEWPORT GB K 111
Riverside Motors Ltd
Riverside Works
Little London
Newport PO30 5BT
Tel: 0983 522552

KENT

ASHFORD GB K 209
Crouch's Garage Ltd
Station Road
Ashford TN23 1PJ
Tel: 0233 23451

ASHFORD GB K 306
Channel Commercials plc
Brunswick Road
Cobbs Wood Estate
Ashford TN23 1EH
Tel: 0233 29271

BROADSTAIRS GB K 116
Thanet Commercials plc
12 Hornet Close
Pysons Road Industrial Estate
Broadstairs
Tel: 0843 603480/602194

CANTERBURY GB K 102
Invicta Motors Ltd
134 Sturry Road
Canterbury CT1 1DR
Tel: 0227 762783

CANTERBURY GB K 204
Lucas Service UK Ltd
Marynard Road
Wincheap Industrial Estate
Canterbury CT1 3RH
Tel: 0227 453510

CRAYFORD GB N 335
Kent DAF Trucks Ltd
Acorn Industrial Park
Crayford Road
Crayford DA1 4AL
Tel: 0322 56415

DARTFORD GB N 105
K T Trucks Ltd
Dartford Industrial Estate
Hawley Road
Dartford DA1 1NQ
Tel: 0322 29331

ERITH GB N 226
South Eastern Auto Electrical Services Ltd
Unit 26
Manford Industrial Estate
Erith
Tel: 0622 69004

MAIDSTONE GB K 105
Drake and Fletcher Ltd
Parkwood Sutton Road
Maidstone ME15 9NW
Tel: 0622 55531

MAIDSTONE GB K 222
South Eastern Auto Electrical Service Ltd
Wharf Road
Tovil
Maidstone ME15 6RT
Tel: 0622 690004

MAIDSTONE GB K 303
Volvo (GB) Ltd
T/A Maidstone Commercials Ltd
Beddow Way
Forstal Road
Aylesford
Maidstone ME20 7BT
Tel: 0622 70811

ST MARY'S HOO GB K 118
Squires & Knight
Fenn Corner
St Mary's Hoo
Nr. Rochester ME3 8RF
Tel: 0634 271987

SITTINGBOURNE GB K 212
Sparshatts of Kent Ltd
Unit 10
Eurolink Industrial Estate
Murston
Sittingbourne ME10 3RN
Tel: 0795 79571

TONBRIDGE GB N 101
Stormont Engineering Co Ltd
Commercial Vehicle Division
Hildenborough
Tonbridge TN118NN
Tel: 0732 833005

TUNBRIDGE WELLS GB K 107
J Rawson (Trucks) Ltd
Longfield Road
Tunbridge Wells TN2 3EY
Tel: 0892 515333

TUNBRIDGE WELLS GB K 224
Lucas Service UK Ltd
North Farm Road
High Brooms Industrial Estate
Tunbridge Wells TN2 3EA
Tel: 0892 510800

LANCASHIRE

ACCRINGTON GB C 220
Gilbraith Commercials Ltd
Market Street
Church
Accrington BB5 0DN
Tel: 0254 31431

ACCRINGTON GB C 124
Lynch Truck Services Ltd
Unit 3, Plot 8
Newhouse Road
Huncoat Industrial Estate
Accrington BB5 6NT
Tel: 0254 301331

BLACKBURN GB C 305
Fox Commercial Vehicles Ltd
Navigation Garage
Forrest Street
Blackburn
Tel: 0254 675111

BLACKPOOL GB C 131
Nortons of Cleveleys
Red Marsh Industrial Estate
Thornton
Cleveleys
Blackpool FY5 4HP

BURNLEY GB C 329
Burnley and Pendle Transport Company Ltd
Queensgate
Colne Road
Burnley BB10 1HH

CHORLEY GB C 114
Gilbraith Commercials Ltd
Botany Bay
Chorley PR 6 8X
Tel: 02572 76421

CLITHEROE GB C 229
Steadplan Ltd
Salthill Industrial Estate
Clitheroe BB7 1QL
Tel: 0200 27415

DARWEN GB C 126
Walsh & Midgley
Bull Hill
Darwen BB3 2TT
Tel: 0254 74356

FORTON GB C 128
Cabus Garage
A6 Lancaster Road
Forton
Lancashire
Tel: 0524 791417

HAYDOCK GB C 325
Haydock Commercial Vehicles Ltd
Yew Tree Trading Estate
Kilbuck Lane
Haydock
Tel: 0942 714103

LANCASTER GB C 317
Pye Motors Ltd
Parliament Street
Lancaster LA1 1DA
Tel: 0524 63553

LEYLAND GB C 500
Leyland DAF Ltd
Leyland Service Centre
Croyston Road
Leyland PR5 1SN
Tel: 0772 421400

LITTLE HOOLE GB C 109
BRS Northern Ltd
Liverpool Road
Little Hoole
Nr. Preston PR4 5JT
Tel: 0772 617668

PRESTON GB C 230
Lucas Service Ltd
160-164 Lancaster Road
Preston PR1 1SR
Tel: 0772 58326

PRESTON GB C 303
Ribblesdale Auto-Electrics Ltd
Marsh Lane
Preston
Tel: 0772 555011

PRESTON GB C 127
Leyland Auto Electrical and Diesel Ltd
Unit 220
Walton Summit Industrial Estate
Bamber Bridge
Preston
Tel: 0772 38583

PRESTON GB C 328
Ryland Vehicle Group Preston
Unit 224
Walton Summit Centre
Bamber Bridge
Preston

ROCHDALE GB C 201
Tom Mellor Ford
Durham Street
Rochdale OL11 1LR
Tel: 0706 355355

LEICESTERSHIRE

BLABY GB E 120
BRS Midlands Ltd
Lutterworth Road
Blaby LE8 3DU
Tel: 0533 773373

HINCKLEY GB E 210
Paynes Garages Ltd
Watling Street
Hinckley LE10 3ED
Tel: 0455 38911

LEICESTER GB E 206
Cossington Commercial Vehicles Ltd
System Road
Cossington
Leicester LE7 8UZ
Tel: 0533 607111

LEICESTER GB E 217
A. B. Butt Ltd
Frog Island
Leicester LE3 5AZ
Tel: 0533 513344

LEICESTER GB E 300
Batchelor Bowles & Co Ltd
Freemens Common
Aylstone Road
Leicester LE2 7SL
Tel: 0533 557667

LEICESTER GB E 305
Ford and Slater of Leicester
Hazel Drive
Narborough Road South
Leicester LE3 2JG
Tel: 0533 896561

LOUGHBOROUGH GB E 106
Charnwood Trucks Ltd
M1 Truck Centre
Ashby Road
Shedshed
Loughborough LE12 5BR
Tel: 0509 502121

LINCOLNSHIRE

BOSTON GB E 204
C F Parkinson Ltd
Fydell Crescent Workshop
Fydell Crescent
Boston PE21 8QY
Tel: 0205 63008

LINCOLN GB E 102
John Longden Ltd
Crofton Road
Lincoln LN3 4PJ
Tel: 0522 38811

LINCOLN GB E 203
C F Parkinson Ltd
Outer Circle Road
Lincoln LN2 4HU
Tel: 0522 30176

LINCOLN GB E 224
Ford & Slater of Lincoln
Sleaford Road
Bracebridge Heath
Lincoln LN4 2NQ
Tel: 0522 22231

LINCOLN GB E 316
Charles Warner Ltd
Outer Circle Road
Lincoln LN2 4LD
Tel: 0522 31785

SPALDING GB F 308
R C Edmondson (Spalding) Ltd
St Johns Road
Spalding
Tel: 0775 67651

GREATER LONDON

ALPERTON GB N 311
Godfrey Davis (London) Ltd
374 Ealing Road
Alperton
Middlesex HA0 1HG
Tel: 01-997 3388

BARKING GB N 216
Dagenham Motors (1981) Ltd
51 River Road
Barking IG11 0SW
Tel: 01-592 6655

BARKING GB N 322
Gifford Tachograph Services & Commercial Ltd
77a River Road
Barking IG11 0DR
Tel: 01-594 4781

CHARLTON GB N 332
Henleys London Ltd
Units 5 & 9
Maritime Industrial Estate
Horizon Way
Charlton SE7 7AY

CHINGFORD GB N 334
Rydale Truck & Coach Ltd
47 Sewardstone Road
Chingford E4 7PU
Tel: 01-529 8686

CROYDON GB N 200

Dees of Croydon Ltd
Dees Commercial Centre
2 Imperial Way
Croydon CR0 4RR
Tel: 01-881 6711

CROYDON GB N 338

C. Barber & Sons Ltd
Barbers Tachograph Centre
87 Beddington Lane
Croydon CR0 4TD
Tel: 01-689 4414

CHISWICK GB N 227

LRT Bus Engineering Ltd
566 Chiswick High Road
Chiswick W4 5R
Tel: 01-994 7024

DAGENHAM GB N 111

Lancaster Trucks Ltd
Lakeside Estate
Heron Way
West Thurrock RM16 1WJ
Tel: 0708 861321

ENFIELD GB N 100

Hunter Vehicles Ltd
Unit 7
Trafalgar Trading Estate
Jeffreys Road
Enfield
Tel: 01-805 5175

ENFIELD GB N 228

Arlington Motor Co Ltd
Mollison Avenue
Brimsdown
Enfield EN3 7NE
Tel: 01-804 1266

FELTHAM GB N 223

Heathrow Commercials Ltd
Staines Road
Bedfont
Feltham TW14 8RP
Tel: 0784 243571

GREENFORD GB N 225

Normand Commercial Vehicles Ltd
Auriol Drive
Oldfield Lane
Greenford
Tel: 01-578 5588

HAYES GB N 213

Dagenham Motors (Hayes) Ltd
Dawley Road
Hayes UB3 1EH
Tel: 01-573 2209

ISLEWORTH GB N 224

Currie Trucks Ltd
207/209 Worton Road
Isleworth TW7 6DS
Tel: 01-568 4343

LONDON GB N 336

The Londoners Tacho Centre Ltd
1A Brabourn Grove
Peckham SE15 2BS
Tel: 01-639 1211

LONDON GB N 201

Arlington Motor Co Ltd
Brentfield Road
Willesden NW10 8HH
Tel: 01-956 5982

LONDON GB N 315

Southern BRS Ltd
Victory Place
Balfour Street SE17 1PH
Tel: 01-703 5071

LONDON GB N 316

BRS Southern Ltd
Leyton Repair Centre
Ruckholt Lane
Leyton E10 5PB
Tel: 01-539 1298

LONDON GB N 327

Transfleet Services Ltd
17 Western Road
Western Trading Estate
Park Royal NW10 7LT
Tel: 01-961 5225

LONDON GB N 318

Hunts Trucks (Wandsworth) Ltd
394 York Road
Wandsworth SW18 1SH
Tel: 01-871 3021

LONDON GB K 225

A23 Tacho Centre Ltd
146/156 Brixton Hill
London SW2 1SD

LONDON GB N 235

London Buses (West Ham Garage)
Greengate Street
London E13

WEMBLEY GB N 103

Henleys (West London) Ltd
Commercial House
Queensbury Road
Wembley
Middlesex HA0 1PG
Tel: 01-998 2121

GREATER MANCHESTER

BOLTON GB C 118
Harris Road Services Ltd
Raikes Lane Industrial Estate
Manchester Road
Bolton BL3 2NS
Tel: 0204 32441

BOLTON GB C 224
Harper Gordon Trucks
Weston Street
Bolton BL3 2BZ
Tel: 0204 31541

BOLTON GB C 308
BRS Northern Ltd
Kay Street
Bolton VL1 2HX
Tel: 0204 394655

HYDE GB C 120
D Hulme Ltd
Broadway Industrial Estate
Dukinfield Road
Hyde SK14 4QZ
Tel: 061-366 9400

MANCHESTER GB C 130
Harith Commercials Ltd
Trafford Park Road
Trafford Park M17 1NJ
Tel: 061-848 8331

MANCHESTER GB C 309
Manchester Garages (Trucks) Ltd
Gorton Lane
Gorton M18 8BT
Tel: 061-223 7131

MANCHESTER GB C 123
Chatfield Martin Walter Ltd
T/A C.G.L. Truck Services
Ashburton Road East
Trafford Park M17 1GT
Tel: 061-872 6855

MANCHESTER GB C 327
H & J Quick Ltd
Moseley Road
Trafford Park M17 1PG
Tel: 061-872 7711

MANCHESTER GB C 204
Chatfields of Manchester
40-46 Ashton Old Road
Ardwick M12 6NA
Tel: 061-273 7351

MIDDLETON GB C 324
West Pennine Trucks Ltd
Stakehill Industrial Estate
Middleton M24 2RL
Tel: 061-653 9700

OLDHAM GB C 111
Main Line Trucks Manchester Ltd
Fields New Road
Chadderton
Oldham OL9 8NH
Tel: 061-652 4218

SALFORD GB C 234
Salford Leyland DAF Ltd
West Egerton Street.
Salford M5 4DY

STRETFORD GB C 223
Lucas Service UK Ltd
Severnside Trading Estate
Textilose Road
Trafford Park M17 1WB
Tel: 061-864 1719

STRETFORD GB C 129
BRS Northern Engineering
Barton Dock Industrial Estate
Barton Dock Road
Stretford M32 0XP
Tel: 061-872 7551

MERSEYSIDE

LIVERPOOL GB C 105
H Woodward and Son plc
334 Rice Lane
Liverpool L9 2BN
Tel: 07048 78121

LIVERPOOL GB C 501
J Blake & Co Ltd
178 Lodge Lane
Liverpool L8 0QW
Tel: 051-727 4501

LIVERPOOL GB C 205
Lucas Service UK Ltd
Vandries Road
Liverpool L3 7BJ
Tel: 051-236 7063

LIVERPOOL GB C 307
Stormont (Merseyside) Ltd,
Hawthorn Road,
Bootle
Liverpool L20 9DA
Tel: 051-922 8481

LIVERPOOL GB C 314
Thomas Hardie Commercials Ltd
Newstet Road
Knowsley Industrial Park (North)
Nr Liverpool L33 7TJ
Tel: 051-546 5291

LIVERPOOL GB C 215
Perris & Kearon Ltd
173-175 Crown Street
Liverpool L7 3LZ
Tel: 051-709 4262

ST HELENS GB C 113
Roberts Motors Ltd
St Helens Ford
City Road
St Helens WA10 6NZ
Tel: 0744 26381

ST HELENS GB C 306
Road Vehicles Ltd
Beaufort Street
Peasley Cross
St Helens WA9 3BQ
Tel: 0744 34343

NORFOLK

DISS GB F 204
Trumber Truck Care Ltd
57 Victoria Road
Diss IP22 3JD
Tel: 0379 52161

FAKENHAM
R. C. Edmondson (Fakenham)
Oak Street
Fakenham NR21 9DU
Tel: 0328 2317

GREAT YARMOUTH GB F 306
L G Perfect (Engineering) Ltd
Jubilee Works
Hafreys Road
Great Yarmouth NR31 0JL
Tel: 0493 650493

KING'S LYNN GB F 112
GDM Transport Engineering Ltd
Leyland Truck Centre
Maple Road
Kings Lynn PE34 3AH
Tel: 0553 761112

KING'S LYNN GB F 310
BRS Southern Ltd
Oldmeadow Road
Hardwich Trading Estate
King's Lynn PE30 4TZ
Tel: 0553 773671

NORWICH GB F 206
Lucas Services UK Ltd
Weston Road North
Norwich NR3 3TL
Tel: 0603 410301

NORWICH GB F 305
Ford and Slater of Norwich
Roundtree Way
Mousehold Lane
Norwich NR7 8SJ
Tel: 0603 49451

NORWICH GB F 313
Busseys Ltd
Whiffler Road
Norwich NR3 2AW
Tel: 0603 44022

NORWICH GB F 116
Carrow Commercials Ltd
Unit 8 Industrial Estate
Kerrison Road
Norwich NR1 1JA

THETFORD GB F 309
B & B Motor Repairs Ltd
Caxton Eay
Thetford IP24 3RY
Tel: 0842 4388

NORTHAMPTONSHIRE

DAVENTRY GB E 119
Daventry Trucks Ltd
Unit 3, Plant House
Royal Oakway North
Daventry NN11 5PQ
Tel: 0327 77009

KETTERING GB E 109
John R Billows (Sales) Ltd
Pytchley Road Industrial Estate
Kettering NN15 6JJ
Tel: 0536 516233

NORTHAMPTON GB E 108
Grose Ltd
Queens Park Parade
Kingsthorpe
Northampton
Tel: 0604 712525

NORTHAMPTON GB E 211
Northampton Diesel & Electrical Services Ltd
Holloway Industrial Estate
Weedon Road
Northampton NN5 5DG
Tel: 0604 55321

NORTHAMPTON GB E 318
Arlington Motor Co Ltd
Bedford Road
Northampton NN1 5NS
Tel: 0604 250151

NORTHAMPTON GB E 208
Airflow Streamlines plc
Letts Road
Northampton NN4 9HQ
Tel: 0604 581121

WELLINGBOROUGH GB E 101
Brookside Garages (Wellingborough) Ltd
Finedon Road
Wellingborough NN8 4BN
Tel: 0933 76651

WELLINGBOROUGH GB E 310
E Ward (Wellingborough) Ltd
Truck Division
Northampton Road
Wellingborough NN8 3PP
Tel: 0933 227878

NORTHUMBERLAND

BERWICK UPON TWEED GB A 308
Cochranes Garage (Tweedmouth) Ltd
Tweedside Trading Estate
Berwick Upon Tweed TD15 2XF
Tel: 0289 305585

CHOPPINGTON GB B 217
Heathline Commercials Ltd
Stakeford Lane
Choppington NE62 5QJ
Tel: 0670 824006

NOTTINGHAMSHIRE

BEESTON GB E 116
Barton Transport plc
61 High Road
Chilwell
Beeston NG9 4AD
Tel: 0602 254881

HOVERINGHAM GB E 110
Tarmac Roadstone Ltd. East Midlands
Hoveringham Tachograph Centre
Hoveringham
Lowdham NG14 7JY
Tel: 0602 663197

HUCKNALL GB E 107
K & M (Hauliers)
T/A Nevilles Garage Ltd
The Aerodrome
Watnall Road
Hucknall NG15 6EN
Tel: 0602 630630

NEWARK GB E 220
C F Parkinson (Notts) Ltd
Brunel Drive
Northern Industrial Estate
Newark NG24 2EG
Tel: 0636 72631

NOTTINGHAM GB E 317
Hooley's Garage Ltd
Abbey Street
Lenton
Nottingham NG7 2PP
Tel: 0602 786145

NOTTINGHAM GB E 121
Sherwood Leyland DAF Ltd
522 Derby Road
Lenton
Nottingham NG7 2GX

NOTTINGHAM GB E 225
R H Commercial Vehicles Ltd
Lenton Lane
Nottingham NG7 2NR

STAPLEFORD GB E 209
Sandcliffe Garage Ltd
Nottingham Road
Stapleford NG9 8AU
Tel: 0602 395000

SUTTON-IN-ASHFIELD GB E 312
Evans Halshaw (Sutton) Ltd
Station Road
Sutton-in-Ashfield NG 17 5FH
Tel: 0623 511511

WORKSOP GB E 313
J T Hunt (Workshop) Ltd
Claylands Avenue
Worksop S18 7BQ
Tel: 0909 475561

OXFORDSHIRE

BANBURY GB E 118
Banbury Trucks Ltd
Unit One, Tuston House
Station Approach
Banbury OX16 8MB
Tel: 0295 67528

BANBURY GB K 312
Hartford Motors (Banbury) Ltd
98 Warwick Road
Banbury OX16 7AH
Tel: 0293 67711

KIDLINGTON GB N 112
Hartwells of Oxford Ltd
Langford Lane
Kidlington OX5 1RY
Tel: 08675 71511

OXFORD GB E 215
Evenlode Truck Centre Ltd
Eynsham Road
Cassington
Oxford OX5 1DD
Tel: 0865 881581

OXFORD GB E 213
City Motors (Oxford)Ltd
Botley Road
Oxford OX2 0PR
Tel: 0865 722455

OXFORD GB K 311
Hartford Motors (Oxford) Ltd
Besselsleigh Road
Nr Wootton
Abingdon OX13 6TP
Tel: 0865 736377

SHROPSHIRE

SHREWSBURY GB D 116
Furrows Commercial Vehicles Ltd
Emmerdale Road
Harlescott Industrial Estate
Shrewsbury SY1 3NP
Tel: 0743 57971

SHREWSBURY GB D 212
Lucas Services UK Ltd
Lancaster Road
Harlescott
Shrewsbury SY1 3NJ
Tel: 0743 55061

TELFORD GB D 320
Furrows Commercial Vehicles Ltd
Halesfield
Telford
Tel: 0952 584433

SOMERSET

FROME GB H 115
Wessex Trucks (Frome) Ltd
Whitworth Road
Marston Trading Estate.
Frome BA11 4BY
Tel: 0373 64970

SHEPTON MALLET GB H 215
Tachograph Services (Shepton Mallet) Ltd
Crowne Trading Estate
Shepton Mallet BA4 5QU
Tel: 0749 3333

TAUNTON GB H 107
White Bros (Taunton) Ltd
Commercial Division
Bathpool
Taunton TA2 8BA
Tel: 0823 74957

TAUNTON GB H 203
H N Hickley & Co Ltd
Tangier
Taunton TA1 4AU
Tel: 0823 5285

TAUNTON GB H 307
National Carriers Fleetcare
Canal Road
Taunton TA1 1PL
Tel: 0823 331151

WINCANTON GB H 219
Wincanton Truck Centre
Aldermeads
Wincanton BA9 9EB
Tel: 0963 33800

YEOVIL GB H 101
Douglas Seaton Ltd
West Hendford
Yeovil BA20 2AG
Tel: 0935 27421

YEOVIL GB H 309
Abbey Hill Vehicle Service
Boundary Road
Lufton Trading Estate
Yeovil
Tel 0935 29111

STAFFORDSHIRE

BURTON UPON TRENT GB D 108
Marley Transport Ltd
Lichfield Road
Branston
Burton upon Trent DE14 3HG
Tel: 0283 712264

BURTON UPON TRENT GB D 317
BRS Midlands Ltd
Derby Street
Burton upon Trent DE14 2LN
Tel: 0283 63702

LICHFIELD GB D 114
TRS (Transport) Ltd
Freeford Bridge
Tamworth Road
Lichfield
Tel: 0543 253421

NEWCASTLE UNDER LYME GB D 314
Hartshorne (Potteries) Ltd
Rosevale Road
Parkhouse Industrial Estate
Newcastle under Lyme ST5 7EF
Tel: 0782 566400

STAFFORD GB D 200
Lloyds Garage Ltd
Stone Road
Stafford ST16 2RA
Tel: 0785 31331

STOKE-ON-TRENT GB D 101
Beeches Garage (1983) Ltd
Leek Road
Hanley
Stoke-on-Trent ST1 6AD
Tel: 0782 23836

STOKE-ON-TRENT GB D 500
Chatfields of Stoke
Commercial Vehicle Division
Clough Street
Hanley
Stoke-on-Trent ST1 4AR
Tel: 0782 202591

STOKE-ON-TRENT GB D 315
Kay's Ltd
Leek New Road
Cobridge
Stoke-on-Trent ST6 2DE
Tel: 0782 264121

STOKE-ON-TRENT GB D 120
Mainline Trucks
High Street
Sandyford
Tunstall
Stoke-on-Trent ST6 5PD
Tel: 0782 575222

STOKE-ON-TRENT GB D 219
BRS Midlands Ltd
Repair Centre
Vernon Road
Stoke-on-Trent ST4 2QF

SUFFOLK

BECCLES GB F 214
Gales Garages Ltd
Common Lane North
Beccles NR34 9QD
Tel: 0502 717023

BURY ST EDMUNDS GB F 115
Chassis-Cabs Ltd
Northern Way
Bury St Edmunds IP52 6NL
Tel: 0284 68570

FELIXSTOWE GB F 311
P & O Roadways Ltd
Surrey Master House
Dock Road
Felixstowe IP11 8QU
Tel: 0394 673272

IPSWICH GB F 114
Marshall (Cambridge) Ltd
Goddard Road
Whitehouse Industrial Estate
Ipswich
Tel: 0437 240200

IPSWICH GB F 210
Lucas Service UK Ltd
Hadleigh Road Industrial Estate
Ipswich IP2 0HB
Tel: 0473 215931

IPSWICH GB F 318
Anglia DAF Trucks Ltd
Unit 32
Claydon Industrial Park
Great Blakenham
Ipswich IP6 0NL

LOWESTOFT GB F 101
Days Garage Ltd
Whapload Road
Lowestoft NR32 1UR
Tel: 0502 65353

STOWMARKET GB F 316
Ro-Truck
Violet Hill Road
Stowmarket IP14 1NN
Tel: 0449 613553

SUDBURY GB F 113
Solar Garage (Ipswich)
Co-operative Society Ltd
Cornard Road
Sudbury CO10 6XA
Tel: 0953 72301

WOODBRIDGE GB F 104
A. G. Potter
New Road
Framlingham
Woodbridge
Tel: 0728 723215

SURREY

EPSOM GB N 321
Cummings & Foster Ltd
T/A Benhill Motors
London Road
Ewell-by-pass
Epsom KT17 2PT
Tel: 01-394 2196

GUILDFORD GB N 207
F G Barnes and Sons Ltd
Slyfield Industrial Estate
Woking Road
Guildford GU1 1RT
Tel: 0483 37731

GUILDFORD GB N 307
Grays Truck Centre Ltd
Slyfield Ind. Est
Woking Road
Guildford GU1 1RY
Tel: 0483 571012

HORLEY GB N 107
Horley Services Ltd
Salfords Industrial Estate
Horley
Nr Redhill RH1 5ES
Tel: 0297 771481

SUSSEX

CHICHESTER GB K 308
Francis Transport Ltd
Portfield Quarry
Shopwyke Road
Chichester PO20 6AD
Tel: 0243 780011

EASTBOURNE GB K 211
Panda Diesels (Newhaven) Ltd
Mountney Bridge
Westham
Nr. Eastbourne
Tel: 0323 767626

HORSHAM GB K 205
Evans Halshaw (Sussex) Ltd
78 Billinghurst Road
Broadbridge Heath
Horsham RH12 3LP
Tel: 0403 56464

HORSHAM GB N 303
Gilbert Rice Ltd
53-55 Bishopric
Horsham RH12 1QJ
Tel: 0403 60465

PORTSLADE GB K 115
Endeavour Motor Co Ltd
Truck Division
Ellen Street
Portslade BN4 1DY
Tel: 0273 418231

SHOREHAM-BY-SEA GB K 207
Evans Halshaw (Sussex) Ltd
44 Dolphin Road
Shoreham-by-Sea BN4 1DY
Tel: 0273 454887

WORTHING GB K 117
I G Bacon Commercials Ltd
Meadow Road Industrial Estate
Worthing
Tel: 0903 204127

TYNE & WEAR

BLAYDON GB B 318
North East DAF Trucks Ltd
Chainbridge Road
Blaydon NE21 5TR
Tel: 091-414 3333

GATESHEAD GB A 109
BRS Northern Ltd
Eastern Avenue
Team Valley Trading Estate
Gateshead NE11 0UU
Tel: 091-487 8844

GATESHEAD GB A 200
Lucas Service UK Ltd
Saltmeadows Road
Gateshead NE8 3BS
Tel: 091-477 3851

NEWCASTLE UPON TYNE GB A 103
Union Trucks Ltd
Mylord Crescent
Killingworth
Newcastle upon Tyne NE12 0UW
Tel: 091-268 3141

NEWCASTLE UPON TYNE GB A 209
Henly's (Newcastle) Ltd
Melbourne Street
Newcastle upon Tyne NE1 2ER
Tel: 091-261 1471

NEWCASTLE UPON TYNE GB A 306
R H Patterson & Co Ltd
Forth Street Works
Newcastle upon Tyne NE1 3PP
Tel: 091-261 2661

SUNDERLAND GB A 307
Cowies of Sunderland
North Hylton Road
Southwick
Sunderland SR5 3HQ
Tel: 091-549 1111

WARWICKSHIRE

ALCESTER GB D 105
Smiths Coaches (Sherington) Ltd
Tything Road
Arden Forest Industrial Estate
Alcester B49 6EX
Tel: 0789 766401

BARFORD GB D 117
Oldhams of Barford
Wellesbourne Road
Barford CV35 8DS
Tel: 0926 624014

RUGBY GB D 123
Noden Truck Centre
3 Avon Industrial Estate
Butlers Leap
Rugby CV21 3UY

WEST MIDLANDS

BIRMINGHAM GB D 121
P J Evans Trucks Ltd
31 Shefford Road
Aston B6 4PQ
Tel: 021-359 8261

BIRMINGHAM GB D 110
Gerard Mann
115-117 Charles Henry Street
Birmingham B12 0SN
Tel: 021-622 3031

BIRMINGHAM GB D 216
Birmingham Trucks Ltd
292 Wharfdale Road
Tyseley B11 2EA
Tel: 021-707 9700

BIRMINGHAM GB D 220
Lucas Service UK Ltd
171 Lichfield Road
Aston B6 5SN
Tel: 021-327 1525

BIRMINGHAM GB D 303
Bristol Street Motors Ltd
Beacon House
Long Acre
Nechells B7 5JJ
Tel: 021-327 4791

BIRMINGHAM GB D 309
Transfleet Services Ltd
Bannerly Street
Garretts Green Industrial Estate
Birmingham B33 0SA
Tel: 021-784 4000

BIRMINGHAM GB D 318
Midlands BRS Ltd
Bromford Mills Branch
Erdington B24 8DP
Tel: 021-328 2200

BRIERLEY HILL GB D 119
Dudley Tachograph Centre Ltd
Thorns Road Trading Estate
Thorns Road
Quarry Bank
Brierley Hill DY5 2JS
Tel: 0384 70301

BROWNHILLS GB D 322
Brownhills Tachograph Centre
Lindon Road
Brownhills WS8 7BW
Tel: 05433 372528

COVENTRY GB D 319
Dawson Freight Commercials Ltd
Unit 1
Eden Street
Coventry CV6 5HE
Tel: 0203 683221

COVENTRY GB D 106
Carwood Motor Units Ltd
Herals Way
Binley
Coventry CV3 2RQ
Tel: 0203 449533

COVENTRY GB D 214
S Jones (Garages) Ltd
Three Spires Industrial Estate
Ibstock Road
Coventry CV6 6BP
Tel: 0203 770617

HALESOWEN GB D 209
Lex Tillotson Birmingham
Park Road
Halesowen B63 2RL
Tel: 0384 822431

WALSALL GB D 111
Maybrook Trucks Ltd
Coppice Lane
Aldridge WS9 9AA
Tel: 0922 56356

WALSALL GB D 206
Tildesley Ford
Northgate
Aldridge WS9 8TH
Tel: 0922 54031

WALSALL GB D 305
Hartshorne Motor Services Ltd
Bentley Mill Close
Walsall
Tel: 0922 720941

WALSALL GB D 306
S Jones (Garages) Ltd
Anglican Road
Aldridge
Walsall WS9 8ET
Tel: 0922 54411

WARLEY GB D 312
Charthire Services Ltd
Pearsall Drive
Oldbury B69 2RA
Tel: 021-544 5125

WEDNESBURY GB D 213
Wincanton Transport Ltd
Heath Estate
Whitworth Close
Darlaston
Wednesbury
Tel: 021-526 3833

WEST BROMWICH GB D 118
Browns Electro-Diesel Co.
Vicarage Road
West Bromwich B71 1AL
Tel: 021-588 3101

WEST BROMWICH GB D 307
Guest Motors Ltd
Old Meeting Street
West Bromwich B70 9SQ
Tel: 021-553 2737

WOLVERHAMPTON GB D 103
Don Everall Motor Sales Ltd
Bilston Road
Wolverhampton WV2 2QE
Tel: 0902 51515

WOLVERHAMPTON GB D 316
A F Glaze Ltd
Dixon Street
Wolverhampton
Tel: 0902 55434

WILTSHIRE

CALNE GB H 113
Blue Rosette Transport Services Ltd
Wenhill Garage
Station Road
Calne
Tel: 0249 816186

CALNE GB H 121
Syms Engineering (Calne) Ltd
Port Marsh Industrial Estate
Calne SN11 9PZ

SALISBURY GB H 501
Westonian Commercials Ltd
Netherhampton
Nr Salisbury
Tel: 0722 744333

SWINDON GB H 109
Howard Tenens (Swindon) Ltd
'D' Building
Parsonage Road
Stratton St Margaret
Tel: 0793 827050

SWINDON GB H 220
Gardiners Auto Electrical Service Ltd
Hawksworth Trading Est.
Swindon SN2 1EE
Tel: 0793 29254

SWINDON GB H 312
BRS Western Ltd
Green Bridge Industrial Estate
Stratton St Margaret
Tel: 0793 29281

WESTBURY GB H 312
Rygor Commercials Ltd
The Broadway
West Wilts Trading Estate
Westbury
Tel: 0373 864334

NORTH YORKSHIRE

BOROUGHBRIDGE GB B 117
Boroughbridge Motors Ltd
Bar Lane
Boroughbridge YO5 9NN
Tel: 0423 322741

MALTON GB B 212
Slaters Transport Ltd
Kirby Misperton
Malton YO17 0UE
Tel: 065 386275

THIRSK GB B 128
Crossroads Commercials Ltd
Stockton Road
Thirsk YO7 1AY

YORK GB B 207
York Autoelectrics Ltd
58 Layerthorpe
York YO3 7YN
Tel: 0904 54513

YORK GB B 307
Polar Motor Co (York) Ltd
Fulford Way
Fulford
York YO1 1YF
Tel: 0904 25371

YORK GB B 126
BRS Northern Ltd
7 James Street
York
YO1 3DW
Tel: 0904 410955

SOUTH YORKSHIRE

BARNSLEY GB B 112
BRS Northern Ltd
Shawfield Road
Carlton Industrial Estate
Barnsley S71 3HS
Tel: 0226 298321

BARNSLEY GB B 305
The Polar Truck Centre
Wombwell Lane
Stairfoot
Barnsley S73 8EG
Tel: 0226 732732

BARNSLEY GB B 205
Cameron Motor Service Centre
Barrowfield Road
Platts Common Trading Estate
Hoyland
Barnsley SL4 9SF
Tel: 0226 742654

DONCASTER GB B 114
Trailer Supermarket (Bawtry) Ltd
Doncaster Road
Bawtry
Doncaster DN10 6NX
Tel: 0302 710711

DONCASTER GB B 310
E G Charlesworth Ltd
Barnby Dunn Road
Wheatly
Doncaster
Tel: 0302 327111

DONCASTER GB B 311
BRS Northern Ltd
Barnsley Road
Doncaster
Tel: 0302 785718

ROTHERHAM GB B 314
Eccles Transport Ltd
Primrose Park
Greasborough Road
Rotherham S60 1RH
Tel: 0709 379289

SHEFFIELD GB B 316
Kirby Phillips Trucks Ltd
Highfield Lane
Sheffield S13 9DB
Tel: 0742 693230

SHEFFIELD GB B 312
Oughtibridge Tachograph Centre
Station Lane
Oughtibridge
Sheffield S30 3HS
Tel: 0742 863881

SHEFFIELD GB B 120
Charles Clark
1 Saville Street
Sheffield S4 7TF
Tel: 0742 766600

SHEFFIELD GB B 201
T C Harrison Group Ltd
Sheffield Truck Operations
Shepcote Lane
Sheffield S9 1TX
Tel: 0742 440051

SHEFFIELD GB B 211
Kirby Central Ltd
Cross Roads
South Anston
Sheffield S31 7ES

SHEFFIELD GB B 214
Lucas Service UK Ltd
300 Savile Street
Sheffield S4 7UD
Tel: 0742 752522

WEST YORKSHIRE

BATLEY GB B 210
Lucas Service UK Ltd
232 Bradford Road
Batley WF17 6LF
Tel: 0924 472415

BRADFORD GB B 125
Long Truck Services Ltd
T/A Northern Coachworks Ltd
Northside Road
Bradford BD7 2BA
Tel: 0274 579262

BRADFORD GB B 300
C D Bramall (Bradford) Ltd
Truck Workshops
Dagenham Road
Cutler Heights Lane
Bradford BD4 9LS
Tel: 0274 682224

BRIGHOUSE GB B 122
Reliance Commercial Vehicles Ltd
Wakefield Road
Brighouse HD6 1QQ
Tel: 0484 712611

CLECKHEATON GB B 115
Crossroads Commercials Ltd
Bradford Road
Gomersal
Cleckheaton BD19 4

HALIFAX GB B 306
Dews Garage Ltd
Northgate
Halifax HX1 1XJ
Tel: 0422 62851

HUDDERSFIELD GB B 309
Brockholes Ltd
Leeds Road
Huddersfield HD2 7UW
Tel: 0484 28111

LEEDS GB B 102
Archbold Truck Sales & Service Ltd
Albert Road
Morley LS27 8TT
Tel: 0532 538511

LEEDS GB B 302
Trimoco Motor Group Ltd
Trimoco Trucks
54 Dolly Lane
Leeds LS9 7NE
Tel: 0532 421222

LEEDS GB B 308
Transfleet Services Ltd
Howley Park Trading Estate
Morley LS27 0BS
Tel: 0532 524422

LEEDS GB B 104
WASS Ltd
123 Hunslett Road
Leeds LS10 1LD
Tel: 0532 439911

LEEDS GB B 202
Sewell of Leeds Ltd
49 Marshall Street
Leeds LS11 9SU
Tel: 0532 435101

LEEDS GB B 127
Charthire Services plc
Parkside Lane
Dewsbury Road
Leeds LS11 5TD
Tel: 0532 773377

PUDSEY GB B 100
Chatfields of Leeds
Grangefield Industrial Estate
Richardshaw Lane
Pudsey LS28 6SO
Tel: 0532 571701

WAKEFIELD GB B 118
Chalderford Motor Co. Ltd
Barnsley Road
Wakefield WF1 5JS
Tel: 0924 370551

SCOTLAND

BORDERS REGION

GALASHIELS GB M 207★
Chalmers McQueen Ltd
Albert Place
Galashiels TD1 3DL
Tel: 0896 2729

CENTRAL

FALKIRK GB M 111
Scottish Road Services Ltd
Burnbank Road
Bainsford
Falkirk FK2 7PD
Tel: 0324 22805

FALKIRK GB M 209
Millar's of Falkirk Ltd
Millar's Truck Centre
North Main Street
Carromshore
Falkirk FK2 8HZ

STIRLING GB M 113
Charthire Service PLC
Whitehouse Road
Springkerse Industrial Estate
Stirling FK7 7SP
Tel: 0786 51761

DUMFRIES & GALLOWAY

DUMFRIES GB M 108
Gateside Commercials (DFS) Ltd
Brownrigg Loaning
Dumfries DG1 3JT
Tel: 0387 61146

DUMFRIES GB M 307
Scottish Road Services Ltd
Glasgow Road
Dumfries DG2 ONY
Tel: 0387 53171

STRANRAER GB M 211★
Western SMT Co Ltd
Lewis Street
Stranraer
Tel: 0776 5174

FIFE

KIRKCALDY GB L 306
Laidlaw (Fife) Ltd
Forth Avenue
Kirkcaldy KY2 5PS

GRAMPIAN

ABERDEEN GB L 204
The Harper Motor Co Ltd
218 Auchmill Road
Bucksburn
Aberdeen AB2 9NB
Tel: 0224 714741

ABERDEEN GB L 302
Aberdeen Trucks Ltd
Greenwell Road
Tullos
Aberdeen
Tel: 0224 873661

ABERDEEN GB L 213
Lucas Service UK Ltd
Units 3 & 4
Girdleness Road
Aberdeen AB1 4DQ

ABERLOUR GB L 206★
McPherson Transport (Aberlour) Ltd
Fisherton Garage
Aberlour AB2 9LB
Tel: 03405 401

ELGIN GB M 116
Scottish Road Services Ltd
Grampian Road
Elgin
Morayshire
Tel: 0343 2171

HUNTLY GB L 304★
Woodside Garage
Knock
Huntly AB5 5LJ
Tel: 046 686 245

HIGHLAND

INVERNESS GB L 201
Macrea and Dick Ltd
36 Academy Street
Inverness
Tel: 0463 238036

INVERNESS GB L 310
Scottish Bus Group Engineering Ltd
64 Seafield Road
Longman Industrial Estate
Inverness 1VI 1TN

TAIN GB L 103★
G Bannerham (Tain) Ltd
Shore Road
Tain
Ross-Shire N19 1EH
Tel: 0862 2480

THURSO GB L 305★
C. Omand
Park Lane
Riverside
Thurso
Caithness

LOTHIAN

BROXBURN GB M 216
Beaverbank Motor Co. Ltd
East Mains Industrial Estate
Broxburn EH52 5AU
Tel: 0506 854834

EDINBURGH GB M 114
FMB (Edinburgh) Ltd
15-19 West Bowling Green Street
Leith
Edinburgh EH6 5NW
Tel: 031-554 1571

EDINBURGH GB M 118
James Bowen & Son Ltd
Newbridge Industrial Estate
Newbridge
Edinburgh EH28 8PJ
Tel: 031-333 5333

EDINBURGH GB M 200
SMT Sales and Service Co Ltd
2 Westfield Avenue
Edinburgh EH11 2RE
Tel: 031-337 9300

LOANHEAD GB M 314
Lothian Trucks Ltd
Straiton
Loanhead EH20 9HQ
Tel: 031-440 4100

STRATHCLYDE

AIRDRIE GB M 213
Central Motors (Calderbank) Ltd
Carlisle Road
Airdrie ML6 8RD
Tel: 023 64 62881

BARRHILL GB M 305★
W & J Barr and Sons (Scotland) Ltd
Braehead
Barrhill KA26 0QR
Tel: 0465 82253

BELLSHILL GB M 117
Laidlaw Trucks (Strathclyde) Ltd
Righead Industrial Estate
Bellshill ML4 3LG
Tel: 0698 747015

BLANTYRE GB M 120
Ailsa Trucks (Northern) Ltd
Whistleberry Road
Blantyre ML3 0ED

CAMPBELTOWN GB M 212★
Martin Maintenance Campbeltown Ltd
Ben Mhor Garage
Saddell Street
Campbeltown
Argyll
Tel: 0586 53155

CUMBERNAULD GB M 301
Scotia DAF Trucks Ltd
8 South Wordpark Court
Wordpark South
Cumbernauld G67 3HE
Tel: 0236 727771

CUMNOCK GB M 103
Kerr and Smith (Cumnock) Ltd
Riverside Garage
Ayr Road
Cumnock KA18 1BJ
Tel: 0290 22440

GLASGOW GB M 115
Charthire Services plc
23 Moss Road
Ayr Road
Glasgow G51 4JT
Tel: 041-440 1889

GLASGOW GB M 201
SMT Sales and Services Co Ltd
149-205 Finnieston Street
Glasgow G3 8HG
Tel: 041-332 6591

GLASGOW GB M 204
Lucas Service Ltd
200-210 Garscube Road
Glasgow G4 9RR
Tel: 041-332 6591

GLASGOW GB M 206
Wylies Ltd
149 Kilbirnie Street
Glasgow G5 8JH
Tel: 041-429 6262

GLASGOW GB M 210
Leyland Bus Ltd
Glasgow Service Centre
2121 London Road
Glasgow G32 8XQ
Tel: 041-778 3491

GLASGOW GB M 215
Ailsa Trucks (Northern) Ltd
101 Kelburn Street
Barrhead
Glasgow G78 2LB
Tel: 041-881 5851

GLASGOW GB M 303
Transfleet Services Ltd
79 Hardgate
Govan
Glasgow G51 4TD
Tel: 041-445 3913

GLASGOW GB M 121
Reliable Vehicles Ltd
Clyde Street
Renfrew
Glasgow PA4 8SL

GLASGOW GB M 110
Callenders Engineering Co Ltd
47 Kirklee Road
Kelvinside
Glasgow G12 0SR
Tel: 041-334 8155

KILMARNOCK GB M 313
Johnston and Drynan
1 Fullarton Street
Kilmarnock KA1 2RB

KILMARNOCK GB M 217
SBG (Engineering) Ltd
Nursery Avenue
Kilmarnock KA1 3JD
Tel: 0563 22551

PAISLEY GB M 306
Clanford Motors Ltd
Clark Street
Paisley PA3 1QZ
Tel: 041-887 0191

TAYSIDE

DUNDEE GB L 101
Dundee Plant Co Ltd
T/A Dundee Truck Centre
411 Clepington Road
Dundee DD3 8ED
Tel: 0382 813644

DUNDEE GB L 105
Camperdown Motor Co Ltd
Kingway West
Dundee DD2 4TD
Tel: 0282 623111

DUNDEE GB L 300
Tayside Tachograph Centre Ltd
Smeaton Road
Wester Goudie
Dundee
Tel: 0382 623263

DUNDEE GB L 212
Bett Trucks Ltd
Faraday Street
Dundee DD2 3QQ
Tel: 0382 817002

PERTH GB L 307
G Mutch Mechanical Services
Shore Road
Perth
Tel: 0738 30291

PERTH GB L 203
Frews Cars Ltd
Riggs Road
Perth PH2 0NT
Tel: 0738 25121

WESTERN ISLES

STORNOWAY GB L 309★
Galston (Stornoway) Motor Services Ltd
Ness Road
Barvas PA86 0QS
Tel: 0851 84269

WALES

CLWYD

COLWYN BAY GB C 107
Gordon Ford
The Trading Estate
Mochdre
Colwyn Bay
Tel: 0492 46756

DEESIDE GB C 326
Thomas Hardie Commercials (North Wales)
Chester Road East
Deeside
Tel: 0244 822707

HOLYWELL GB C 117
Ellis Davis & Son Ltd
Crown Chert Quarry
Trelogan
Holywell CH8 9 BD
Tel: 0745 560320

WREXHAM GB C 231
Unigate plc
Kays Wrexham
Wrexham Road
Rhostyllan
Nr Wrexham LL14 4DP
Tel: 0978 291915

WREXHAM GB C 312
D H Jones (Coal and Haulage) Ltd
Penybont Works
Chirk
Wrexham LL14 JAW
Tel: 0978 823434

DYFED

CARMARTHEN GB G 303
Western BRS Ltd (West Wales Branch)
Heol Alltycrap
Johnstown
Carmarthen SA31 3NE
Tel: 0267 237423

HAVERFORDWEST GB G 105
Merlin Motor Co Ltd
Fishguard Road Industrial Estate
Haverfordwest SA62 4BT
Tel: 0437 2468

LLANFYRNACH GB G 206★
Mansel Davies & Son Ltd
Taffyale Garage
Station Yard
Llanfyrnach SA35 0BZ
Tel: 023 873 631

LLANRHYSTUD GB G 212★
Lewis' Coaches
Bryneithin
Llanrhystud
Tel: 09748 495

MID GLAMORGAN

BRIDGEND GB G 210
BRS Western Ltd
Westerton Road
Bridgend CF31 3YS
Tel: 0656 653331

CAERPHILLY GB G 104
R J Brown Ltd
The Truck Centre
Pontgwindy Industrial Estate
Caerphilly CF8 3HU
Tel: 0222 852222

TREFOREST GB G 301
Griffin Mill Garages Ltd
Upper Boat
Treforest
Nr Pontypridd
Tel: 044385 2216

SOUTH GLAMORGAN

CARDIFF GB G 109
Tanner Tachograph Centre Ltd
C/o W. T. Davies (Transport) Ltd
232 Penarth Road
Cardiff CF1 7XJ
Tel: 0222 33101

CARDIFF GB G 305
Nash of Cardiff
Sloper Road
Grangetown
Cardiff CF1 8TE
Tel: 0222 387221

CARDIFF GB G 213
Lucas Service UK Ltd
Unit 2c
Hadfield Road
Off Penarth Road
Cardiff CF1 8TR
Tel: 0222 28361

WEST GLAMORGAN

SWANSEA GB G 108
City Electrical Diesel Services
Site F 3
Nantyffin Road South
Llansamlet
Swansea
Tel: 0792 792010

SWANSEA GB G 209
Shorts Auto Electrical Services Ltd
43-49 Station Road
Landore
Swansea SA1 2JE
Tel: 0792 469595

SWANSEA GB G 300
Bevan Commercial Vehicles Ltd
18-20 Morfa Road
Hafod
Swansea SA1 2EH
Tel: 0792 50646

GWENT

NEWPORT GB G 103
South Wales Commercials Ltd
Leeway
Spytty Road
Newport NPT OUQ
Tel: 0633 271005

NEWPORT GB G 211
BRS Western Ltd
Watch House Parade
Alexandra Dock
Newport NP9 5YG
Tel: 0633 840083

NEWPORT GB G 306
Evans Halshaw (Newport) Ltd
Ford House
Leeway Industrial Estate
Newport NP1 0QU
Tel: 0633 278020

GWYNEDD

ANGLESEY GB C 320★
Morelog Farm Services
Elim Garage Ltd
Llanfachraeth
Anglesey LL65 4UP
Tel: 0407 740261

CAERNARFON GB C 222★
J T Jones and Sons
Dulyn Motors
Penygroes
Caernarfon
Tel: 0286 880218

POWYS

BRECON GB G 207★
Brecon Motors (DIS) Ltd
The Walton
Rich Way
Brecon LD3 4EG
Tel: 0874 2223

NEWTOWN GB C 216★
Grooms Industries
Pool Road
Newtown SY16 1DL
Tel: 0686 26731

Appendix VII

Useful Addresses

TACHOGRAPH MANUFACTURERS IN UK

Lucas Kienzle Instruments Ltd
36 Gravelly Industrial Park
Birmingham B24 8TA
Tel: 021-328 5533

Veeder-Root Ltd
Kilspindie Road
Dundee DD2 3QJ
Tel: 0382 84161

Time Instrument Manufacturers Ltd
5 Alston Drive
Bradwell Abbey
Milton Keynes MK13 9HA
Tel: 0908 220020

MISCELLANEOUS EQUIPMENT MANUFACTURERS/SUPPLIERS

ICS Black Box (UK) Ltd
Willowbrook Technology Park
St Mellons
Cardiff CF3 0EX
Tel: 0222 770717

Visect Ltd (manufacturers of Tach-Trak)
14 The Moorings
Pill
Bristol BS20 0EG
Tel: 027581 2274

GB Tachopak
Wilton Road
Humberston
Grimsby
South Humberside
Tel: 0472 210102/814291

CHART SUPPLIERS IN UK

Lucas Kienzle Instruments Ltd
36 Gravelly Industrial Park
Birmingham B24 8TA
Tel: 021-328 5533

Veeder-Root Ltd
Kilspindie Road
Dundee DD2 3QJ
Tel: 0382 84161

Tachodisc Ltd
Clarendon Court
Winwick Quay
Warrington
Cheshire WA2 8QP
Tel: 0925 35444/36336

Wightman Mountain Ltd (Chartwell)
142 Vauxhall Street
London SE11 5RH
Tel: 01-582 6522

Charts can be obtained from some commercial stationers and from local offices of the Road Haulage Association (RHA) and Freight Transport Association (FTA).

ANALYSIS SERVICES

AB Butt Ltd
Frog Island
Leicester LE3 5AZ
Tel: 0533 513344

BTAC
Jubilee House
Wapping Road
Bristol BS1 4RH
Tel: 0272 299761

Datamaid Ltd
47 First Avenue
Deeside Industrial Park
Clwyd CH5 2NU
Tel: 0244 823177

Distribution Projects Ltd
Bridgegate Chambers
Duke Street
Chester CH1 1RP
Tel: 0244 313283

Elton Associates
52 Somers Road
Malvern
Worcs WR14 1HT
Tel: 06845 3304

Farnsworth Consultancy
Cannon House
2–3 Wood Terrace
Shelton
Stoke-on-Trent ST1 4LR
Tel: 0782 202088

Foster Tachographs Ltd
88 Market Street West
Preston PR1 4RH
Tel: 0772 555262

Lucas Kienzle Instruments Ltd
36 Gravelly Industrial Park
Birmingham B24 8TA
Tel: 021-328 5533

Mills Associates Ltd
Hilton House
Lord Street
Stockport
Cheshire
Tel: 061-477 4466

Novadata Ltd
108 Bradford Street
Bocking
Braintree
Essex CM7 6AU
Tel: 0376 48963

Ribblesdale Analysing Services
124 Marsh Lane
Preston PR1 8YN
Tel: 0772 27881

Road Transport Computer Services Ltd
West End
Long Whatton
Loughborough
Leicestershire LE12 5DW
Tel: 0509 843746

Rutac Transport Consultancy Ltd
5 Regal House
Mengham Road
Hayling Island
Hants PO11 9LA
Tel: 0705 465914

HG & V Searchline
Graphics House
180a Watling Street
Bridgtown
Cannock
Staffs WS11 3BD
Tel: 0543 466422

TAC Ltd
The Merseyside Innovation Centre
131 Mount Pleasant
Liverpool L3 5TF
Tel: 051-709 4704

Tachdata Ltd
4 High Street
Holywood
Co Down
Northern Ireland BT18 9AZ
Tel: 02317 6548

Tacho-care
18 Fernhill Road
Olton
Solihull
West Midlands B92 7RT
Tel: 021-706 4901

Tachocard Computer Services Ltd
Unit C3
Charles House
Bridge Road
Southall
Middlesex UB2 4BD
Tel: 01-574 4637

Tachodisc Ltd
7 Clarendon Court
Winwick Quay
Warrington
Cheshire WA2 8QP
Tel: 0925 35444/36336

The Tachograph Analysis Bureau
106 Becketts Lane
Great Broughton
Chester CH3 5RP
Tel: 0244 317940

Tachograph Readers Ltd
Rossfield Road
Rossmore Trading Estate
Ellesmere Port LE5 3AW
Tel: 051-355 2101

Ward Associates Ltd
106a Elm Grove
Hayling Island
Hants PO11 9EH
Tel: 0705 469111

Wheel-tech Services
321 Cowbridge Road East
Canton
Cardiff CF5 1JE
Tel: 0222 35651

Wilding Tachoscan
29 Regal Close
Ealing
London W5 2SB
Tel: 01-997 6946

Wirral Tachograph Analysis
2 Broad Lane
Lower Heswall
Wirral L60 9LE
Tel: 051-342 3749

TACHOGRAPH-RELATED SOFTWARE SUPPLIERS

Car Fleet Control Ltd
Cannon House
2255 Coventry Road
Birmingham B26 3NX
Tel: 021-742 8771

Conqueror Business and
Computer Services Ltd
4 Hazelwood Lane
Ampthill
Bedford MK45 2HA
Tel: 0525 405167

Distribution Planning Software Ltd
51a Upper High Street
Cradley Heath
West Midlands B64 5HT
Tel: 0384 638272

Distribution Projects Ltd
Bridgegate Chambers
Duke Street
Chester CH1 1RP
Tel: 0244 313283

Lucas Kienzle Instruments Ltd
36 Gravelly Industrial Park
Birmingham B24 8TA
Tel: 021–328 5533

Microspecific Ltd
3 Pillings Road Industrial Estate
Oakham
Rutland
Leics
Tel: 0572 2528

Mintmove Ltd
Hindley Business Centre
Platt Lane
Hindley
Wigan WN2 3PA
Tel: 0945 522373

Perthcrest Tranman Ltd
28a High Street
Thornbury
Bristol BS12 2AH

QRH Computer Group
Stoneleigh
Halifax Road
Brighouse
West Yorkshire HD6 2AQ
Tel: 0484 710621

Road Tech Computer Systems Ltd
Station Industrial Estate
Imperial Way
Watford
Herts WD2 4YX
Tel: 0923 229266

Synergy Distribution Systems Ltd
Synergy House
Lisle Street
Loughborough LE11 0AY
Tel: 0509 232706

ANALYSIS ASSOCIATIONS

Tachograph Analysis Association
The Innovation Centre
131 Mount Pleasant
Liverpool L3 5TF
Tel: 051-708 0123
    051-709 4704

Inclusion of names in these particular lists does not imply any recommendation by the author or publisher, any guarantee of the suitability of products or services offered, any acknowledgement of the standing of the companies mentioned or their continued existence or involvement in the industry. Readers are advised to make their own checks before using products or services. No responsibility can be accepted by the author or publishers for losses resulting from business dealings with any firm listed here.

These lists are not necessarily comprehensive nor are they intended as a complete buyer's guide to products and services. The author would be pleased to hear from any firm or organisation who would wish their name and address to be included in such listings in any future edition.

Index

Accident-free bonuses, 105
Accidents
  evaluation, 87–98
    accuracy, 87–8
    analysis for, 88–9
    case studies, 89–96, 97, 98
    developments in, 96
    facts revealed, 89
    and witness unreliability, 87
  recordings, 124–5
    as legal evidence, 146–7
ACE Series analysers, 58–9
Activity mode
  driver's legal responsibilities, 136
  standard instrument traces, 47–8
Agricultural vehicle exemptions, 180
Analysers
  disc, 54–5
  driver equipment, 53–4
  electronic, 58–9
  magnifiers, 55–7
  mirror analyser, 57
Analysis
  in accident evaluation, 88–9
  computerised, 60–4
    Carmichael System, 63–4
    Gate Micro Systems, 62–3
    Lucas Kienzle FOS System, 60–2
  legal requirements, 66–7, 68
  see also Charts; Operational analysis
Approvals
  certificate, 177–8
  marks, 177
  type, 164–5

Battery cut-off, 30–1
Black Box, ICS, 159
Bonuses for drivers, accident-free,
  105
Break periods
  analysis, 74
  law on, 183
  recording, 130
British Approvals Service for Electrical
  Equipment in Flammable Atmospheres
  (BASEEFA), 31

Cable routing, 34, 35
Calibration
  checks, 37
  frequency, 37
  microprocessor drive systems, 22
  plaque, examination availability, 138
  records, 37–8
  test, 38–40
  tolerances, 36, 40
  see also Seals

Carmichael computer analysis system,
  63–4
Certificate of approval, 177–8
Charts, 43–5
  inserting, 26–7
  as legal evidence, 146–8
  legal requirements, 43–4, 65–9
    drivers' obligations, 65, 135–41
    employers' obligations, 133–5
    errors, 67, 69
    movement, clock control, 171
    recording examination, 66–7
    signing/retaining, 67
    systematic check, 65–6
    visual check, 66
  primary/secondary positions, 20
  storage/filing/protection, 50, 51–2
  structure, 45
  supply, 43
  swapping, 86
  see also Analysers; Analysis;
    Irregularities in recordings; Record
    sheets; Recordings
Check list for drivers, 138–41
Clock
  calibration testing, 39
  and chart movement requirements, 171
  driver's legal responsibilities, 136
  jammed, 118–19
  legal requirements, 170, 171
  setting, 27–8
  stopping, 85–6
  turned back, 83, 84
Clutch repairs and electronic drive
  systems, 22, 34
Coefficient, characteristic, 40
Community Recording Equipment
  Regulations, *see* Equipment
  Regulations
Computers
  in analysis, 60–4
    Carmichael System, 63–4
    Gate Micro Systems, 62–3
    Lucas Kienzle FOS System, 60–2
  in-cab, 154–8
    Lucas Kienzle system, 155–7
    MAN system, 155
  see also Developments, technological
Cost control, 114
Council Regulation (EEC) No 3821/85, *see*
  Equipment Regulations
Court, *see* Prosecution, tachographs in
Crew, *see* Drivers
Crossed hammers, 24, 136–7

Dashboard fitment, 33, 34
Delays

analysis, 74
typical recording, 131
Deliveries, special, cost of, 115
   see also Loading/unloading equipment
    viability; Multi-drop operation
    planning
Derogation, *see* Exemptions to fitment and
   use
Developments, technological, 148–59
   Black Box, ICS, 159
   computers, in-cab, 154–8
    Lucas Kienzle system, 155–7
    MAN system, 155
   demand, 148–9
   fuel monitoring, 149, 150, 151
   the future, 157
   pace of change, 148
   road speed limiters, 149, 152–4
    legal requirements, 154
   Tach-Trak, 158
Disc analyser, 54–5
Distance
   analysis, 76, 77
   estimation unreliability, 87
   measurement, legal requirements, 170
   recording, 25–6
    area on sheet, 174
    instruments, legal requirements,
     172
    trace, 49
   visual indicator, legal requirements,
    171
Drive systems
   electronic, 22–3
   mechanical, 22
Drivers
   accident-free bonuses, 105
   action on tachograph failure, 143–4
   analysis of, FOS computer, 62
   analysis equipment for, 53–4
   attitudes, 99
   and planning opportunities, 107–8
   chart completion requirements, 44
   hours legislation, 182–5
    break periods, 183
    definitions, 182
    driving limits, 182–3
    emergencies, 185
    rest periods, 183–4
    summary, 185
   legal obligations, 65, 135–41
    chart examination, 101
    checklist, 138–41
    in equipment use, 166–7
    and instrument failure, 167
    offences, 142
   productivity schemes, 102–5
    conditions for, 103
    factors in, 103–5
    reluctance to change, 102–3
   training, 108

two-man operation, 20, 26, 172
Driving
   efficiency, and recording analysis, 76,
    78, 79
   technique optimization, 101–2

EC Regulations, *see* Legislation
Electric vehicle exemption, 180
Electronic instrument connections, 34
Emergencies, and drivers' hours'
   legislation, 185
Employers
   legal responsibilities, 133–5
    in equipment use, 166
    instrument failure, 167
    offences, 142
Engine speed recording, 29–30
   mirror analyser for, 57
Equipment Regulations, 132, 162–78,
   179–81
   approvals
    certificate, 177–8
    mark, 177
    type, 164–5
   characteristics/functions, 169
   construction requirements, 170–4
    closing device, 172
    general, 170–1
    markings, 173
    recording instruments, 171–2
    tolerances, 173–4
    visual instruments, 171
   definitions, 169
   final provisions, 167–8
   installation
    and inspection, 165–6, 176–7
    recording equipment, 175–6
   principles/scope, 163–4
   record sheets, 174–5
   use of equipment, 166–7
   see also Instruments; Legislation
European Court of Justice, 16
   see also Legislation; Prosecution,
    tachographs in
Examination, *see* Inspections/checks
Exemptions to fitment and use, 179–81
   declaration of, 188
   international, 179

Failure of instruments
   legal requirements, 143–4, 167
   warning systems, 28–9
Filing of charts, 50, 51–2
FOS computer analysis system, 60–2
Fourth stylus recordings, 50
   for fuel monitoring, 149, 151
Fuel monitoring technology, 149, 150, 151

Gas vehicle exemption, 180
Gate Micro Systems analysis programs,
   62–3

Gear-change peaks, 80
Gearbox
  adaptor for cable drive, 22, 34
  removal and seal breaking, 22
Goods Vehicles (Plating and Testing)
  Regulations 1988, 187

Hazardous goods/areas and intrinsically
  safe instruments, 30–1
Hours of work legislation, 182–5
  break periods, 183
  definitions, 182
  driving limits, 182–3
  emergencies, 185
  rest periods, 183–4
  summary, 185

ICS Black Box, 159
Illegal recordings, *see* Irregularities in
  recordings
Inspections/checks, 144–5, 176–7
  charts, 66–7, 101
  see also Calibration; Testing
Installation, 33–5
  legislation, 165–6, 176–7
    recording equipment, 175–6
  plaques, 36, 37–8, 41, 166
    legal requirements, 175
Instruments, 19–32
  chart insertion, 26–7
  clock setting, 27–8
  drive systems, 22–3
  electronic, connections, 34
  engine speed recording, 29–30
  failure
    employers'/drivers' legal
      responsibilities, 167
    statutory defences, 143–4
    warning, 28–9
  intrinsically safe, 30–1
  manufacturers, 19–20
  one-man/two-man, 20–2
  recording mechanism, 23–6
    moving, 25–6
    for second crew member, 26
    stationary, 24–5
    trace production, 26
  speed warning light, 28
  see also Developments, technological;
    Equipment Regulations
Intrinsically safe instruments, 30–1
Irregularities in recordings, 82–6
  accidents, 124
  action to be taken, 67, 69
  and chart inspection, 124
  chart swapping, 86
  clock
    jammed, 118–19
    stopped, 85–6
    turned back, 83, 84
  detection of, 55, 57

  visual, 71
  faulty recordings, 121–3
  faulty tachograph, 120–1
  interference, 124
  manual recordings, 84, 85, 125–6
  opening of instrument, 123
    detection, 57
    examples, 123, 127–8
    recording gap, 24
    unexplained, 127–8
  overrun, 23–4, 117
  seizure of records, 145
  speed stylus bent/inhibited, 82–3
  unauthorised vehicle use, 115
Islands, exemptions on, 180

Journey analysis in trunking planning,
  109

Legislation
  on charts, 43–5, 65–9
    drivers' obligations, 65, 135–41
    employers' obligations, 133–5
    errors, 67, 69
    recording examination, 66–7
    signing/retaining, 67
    systematic check, 65–6
    visual check, 66
  charts in legal proceedings, 146
  drivers' hours, 182–5
    break periods, 183
    definitions, 182
    driving limits, 182–3
    emergencies, 185
    rest periods, 183–4
    summary, 185
  enforcement powers, 144–5
  equipment regulations, 132, 162–78
    approvals, 164–5, 177–8
    characteristics/functions, 169
    construction requirements, 170–4
    definitions, 169
    final provisions, 167–8
    installation, 165–6, 175–7
    principles/scope, 163–4
    record sheets, 174–5
    use of equipment, 166–7
  exemptions, 179–81
    international, 179
    national, 179–81
  offences/penalties, 142–3
  statutory defences, 143–4
  UK application, 132–41
    bibliography, 186
    compliance, responsibilities in, 132
    driver's responsibilities, 135–41
    employers' responsibilities, 133–5
    regulations in, 132
    road speed limiters, 154
  see also European Court of Justice;
    Prosecution, tachographs in

Loading/unloading equipment viability, 110–11
Local delivery, *see* Multi-drop operation planning

M/FOS analyser, 59
Magnifiers, 55–7
Manual entries
  illegal, 84, 85, 125–6
  legal, 137–8
Manufacturers, 19–20
Microprocessor based drive system, 22–3
Mirror analyser, 57
Motorways
  driving on, 76
  and route planning, 114
Multi-drop operation planning, 112–14
  schedule plotting, 113
  typical recording, 129

New technology, *see* Developments, technological

Opening of instrument
  illegal, 123
    and clock turned back, 83, 84
    detection, 57
    examples, 123, 127–8
    recording gap, 24
    unexplained, 127–8
  legal
    for chart insertion, 26–7
    recording of, 26, 172
Operational analysis, 70–86
  chart analysis, 80–1
    data record format, 81
  information revealed, 72–80
    break periods, 74
    distance, 76, 77
    list of, 72
    speed recordings, 72, 78–80
    stationary time, 75
    time, 80
    travelling time, 75–6
    working times, 72–4
  options compared, 70–1
  regular monitoring advantages, 71–2
  visual scan, 71
  see also Irregularities in recordings; Planning and tachographs
Overrun recordings, 23–4, 117

Passenger and Goods Vehicles (Recording Equipment) Regulations 1979, 132
Planning and tachographs, 106–15
  ancillary equipment viability, 110–11
  cost control, 114
  data use, 108–9
  multi-drop operations, 112–14
    schedule plotting, 113
  need for, 106–7

potential of the tachograph in, 107–8
  pre-tachograph days, 106
  route planning, 114
  special deliveries, 115
  and training needs, 108
  trunking operations, 109–10
  unauthorised vehicle use, 115
  vehicle utilisation, 111–12
    spare vehicle, 114–15
  see also Operational analysis
Plaques
  calibration, examination availability, 138
  descriptive, statutory information on, 173
  installation, 36, 37–8, 166
  see also Approvals
Police, statutory chart examination, 101
Postal vehicle exemptions, 181
Productivity schemes and the tachograph, 102–5
  conditions for, 103
  reluctance to change, 102–3
Prosecution, tachographs in
  accident case studies, 89–96, 97, 98
  for speeding, 99–100
  see also European Court of Justice
Public Service Vehicle exemptions, 179, 180, 181

Record sheets, legal requirements, 174–5
Recording mechanism, 23–6
  moving, 25–6
  stationary, 24–5
    automatic instrument, 24–5
    standard instrument, 24
  trace production, 26
Recordings, 45–50
  automatic instrument, 49
  and chart structure, 45
  distance, 25–6
    area on sheet, 174
    instruments, legal requirements, 172
    trace, 49
  examination, legal requirements, 66–7
  fourth-stylus, 50
  standard instrument, 45–9
    activity, 47–8
    distance, 49
    speed, 48
  typical, 129–131
  see also Charts; Irregularities in recordings
Regulations, *see* Legislation
Rest periods, law on, 183–4
Road speed limiters, 149, 152–54
  legal requrements, 154
Road Vehicles (Construction and Use) Regulations 1986, 154
Rodgers, William, 16

INDEX

Route planning, 114

Safe instruments, 30–1
Safety in Mines Research Establishment
  (SMRE), 31
Seals, 36–7
  breaking, and clutch repairs, 22, 34
  information on, 40–1
  legal requirements, 176
  special marks on, 165
  see also Calibration
Special deliveries, cost of, 115
Speed
  average, calculation, 45
  estimation unreliability, 87
  limiters, 149, 152–4
    legal requirements, 154
  measurement, legal requirements, 170
  recording
    area on sheet, 174
    instruments, legal requirements,
      172
    operational analysis, 76, 78–80
    trace, standard instrument, 48
    visual indicator, legal requirements,
      171
  warning light, 28
  see also Engine speed recording
Speeding, tachograph evidence, 99–101,
  146
Speedometer replacement, 33
Speeds, for calibration testing, 39
Stationary time, analysis, 75
Statutory defences, 143–4
Storage of charts, 50, 51–2

Tach-Trak, 158
Testing
  annual, UK, 187–8

standard conditions, 177
  see also Calibration
Time
  drivers' hours legislation, 182–5
  measurement, legal requirements, 170
  recording
    analysis, 72–4
    areas on sheet, 174
    instruments, legal requirements,
      172
    setting, 27–8
    travelling, analysis, 75–6
    visual indicator, legal requirements,
      171
Tolerances
  calibration, 36, 40
  equipment construction requirements,
    173–4
Traces, see Recordings
Tractor exemption, 180
Trade unions, early attitudes, 15–16
Traffic jams, 80
Training drivers/management, 108
Transport Act, 1968, 15, 132
Travelling time, analysis, 75–6
Treaty of Rome, 16
Trunking operations, planning, 109–10
Two-man operation, 20, 26
  time recording requirements, 172

Vehicle analysis, FOS computer, 62
Vehicle utilization planning, 111–12
  spare vehicles, 114–15

Warning systems
  failure, 28–9
  speed, 28
Wheel circumference and calibration, 40
Workshops, approved, 41–2

List of Advertisers

Eversheds Limited	6
GB Tachopak	8
Lucas Kienzle Instruments Ltd	32